MATHEMATICS ESSENTIAL
FOR ELEMENTARY STATISTICS

MATHEMATICS ESSENTIAL FOR ELEMENTARY STATISTICS

A SELF-TEACHING MANUAL

BY

HELEN M. WALKER, Ph.D.

ASSISTANT PROFESSOR OF EDUCATION
TEACHERS COLLEGE, COLUMBIA UNIVERSITY

NEW YORK
HENRY HOLT AND COMPANY

PREFACE

Purpose. In this modern era of specialization it is not uncommon for a person who is a scholar in one field to be a layman, sometimes an all but illiterate layman, in another field. This book is written for the adult layman who has forgotten his elementary mathematics and who finds that fact a handicap in studying statistical method. Our graduate schools today are full of mature, intelligent men and women who have had no intimate acquaintance with mathematics for years, and who are now discovering that in order to understand the modern world, in order to read the rapidly expanding literature of their own fields, they need to become conversant with statistical method. But statistical method, even in its simpler phases, is a branch of applied mathematics. Refusal to admit this fact will not lessen the difficulties which await the student who is unable to think competently in numerical and symbolic forms.

Origin. This text is the outcome of several years of work in analyzing the difficulties of about one thousand graduate students of statistical method, in devising prognostic and diagnostic tests for them, and in studying the relationship between scores on these tests and class work. These materials have been tried out by my own students in first year statistics courses, courses in which the primary goal is the development of statistical concepts, critical judgment and interpretive ability, and in which the algebraic aspects of the work, and the amount of computation required have been held to a minimum. My students use these units voluntarily and avidly, with two very obvious results: The class as a whole has been able to cover more ground in statistics than was possible before the units were available; and the weaker students who formerly felt a distinct strain are achieving a new sense of confidence and a better comprehension of the statistical concepts studied. Through spending time on definite background work, they have saved the time which might otherwise have been fruitlessly consumed by erroneous computation, slowness, anxiety, haziness of thinking, and by inability to read a text because of failure to comprehend symbolic language.

Scope. With the exception of the calculus, the book contains all those topics which contribute most directly to elementary statistical method. It includes the mathematical background needed for the understanding of any statistics text likely to be used in a course for which the calculus is not a prerequisite. It presupposes very little knowledge of mathematics, even giving a review of certain arithmetic topics ordinarily taught below the eighth grade. On the other hand it includes material, algebraic in nature, but unfamiliar to the average teacher of secondary mathematics. Its emphases are radically different from those of an ordinary text in algebra. It stresses the idea of summation and the ability to use symbolism creatively as a language; develops such concepts as variable, parameter, and residual; introduces the idea of least squares; discusses homogeneity among moments; and derives a number of simple statistical formulas.

Plan. The arrangement of the book permits a rapid review of those topics with which a student has once been familiar, and enables him to omit those topics he has already mastered, and to discover quickly those sections containing material he does not know. Each chapter [1] begins with an exploratory self-scoring test, answers for which are provided in a key at the back of the book. The student who makes no errors on this test may assume that it is unnecessary for

[1] With the exception of Chapter VI, XIII, XIV, XX, and XXI.

him to spend further time on this unit, and may proceed at once to the next unit. The student for whom this preliminary test presents difficulties will go on to the explanatory and practice material which follow the test. After completing these, he will come to a second test, similar in content and difficulty to the first one, by which he can judge his progress.

The content of the book is organized on two levels. Part I furnishes a minimum list of topics which will be needed by students in the more elementary courses in statistical method and measurements. Part II presents additional and somewhat more difficult material designed to furnish an adequate mathematical background for the study of any text in statistical method which does not require the calculus for its understanding. The mastery of this second part would greatly aid in clarifying the thinking of the beginner in statistical work, but it can be omitted by those who wish to cover only the topics most urgently needed.

Acknowledgments. I am indebted to many of my students for constructive suggestions and insight into the mathematical difficulties encountered in statistical method. In particular I am indebted to Dr. Randolph B. Smith, H. Gray Funkhouser, and the late Robert Mendenhall, all of whom were my teaching associates during the period when the manuscript was in preparation and who furnished much helpful criticism; to Dr. Jack Dunlap, who tried out parts of the material in his classes at Fordham University; to Miss Inez Morris and Dr. Ralph Brown, whose careful checking of the entire manuscript was invaluable; and to Miss Florence Ropp and Miss Caroline Draper, whose competent typing facilitated the work.

H. M. W.

Columbia University
January 1, 1934

CONTENTS

PART ONE

CONTENTS

MATHEMATICS ESSENTIAL
FOR ELEMENTARY STATISTICS

PART ONE

I

ORDER OF ARITHMETIC OPERATIONS

Initial Test

This introductory test is to help you discover whether you need practice on this aspect of computation. Place a plus sign at the left of each correct statement and a minus sign at the left of each incorrect statement. After you have marked the test, compare your answers with those in the key at the back of the book. If you have made the computations quickly and without error, go on at once to Chapter II. If you have made errors or have been obliged to work slowly, study the explanations and practice material given below. Then take the second test to measure the amount of improvement you have made. The two tests are of about the same difficulty. To get the best measure of the amount of improvement you have made, allow several hours to elapse after you study the practice material and before you take the second test.

1. $3+4+7=7+3+4$

2. $3+42\div5=9$

3. $12(\frac{3}{4})=3(\frac{12}{4})$

4. $12\div3+2=2\frac{2}{5}$

5. $64\div(16\times2)=8$

6. $(\frac{3}{4})^2=\frac{9}{16}$

7. $(\frac{2}{3})(\frac{5}{4})(\frac{3}{10})=(\frac{2}{4})(\frac{5}{10})(\frac{3}{3})$

8. $25\div2+3=5$

9. $\frac{1}{4}(1-\frac{3}{2})=\frac{1}{4}-\frac{3}{8}$

10. $\frac{(4+8)}{3}=\frac{4}{3}+\frac{8}{3}$

11. $\frac{(4+8)}{(3\times2)}=\frac{4}{3}+\frac{8}{2}$

12. $\frac{(4\times8)}{(3\times2)}=\frac{4}{3}\times\frac{8}{2}$

13. $\frac{(4+8)}{(3+2)}=\frac{4}{3}+\frac{8}{2}$

14. $\frac{(6\times5\times7)}{3}=2\times5\times7$

3

15. $\dfrac{(4\times5)}{3}=\dfrac{4}{3}\times\dfrac{5}{3}$

16. $\sqrt{25+16}=5+4$

17. $5(2-\tfrac{1}{15})=10-\tfrac{1}{3}$

18. $\sqrt{1-(0.6)^2}=0.8$

19. $\dfrac{4+3}{3}=\dfrac{4}{3}+1$

20. $\dfrac{36+5}{6}=6+5$

21. $\tfrac{1}{2}(5\times7)=(\tfrac{5}{2})(\tfrac{7}{2})$

22. $5+(\tfrac{3}{2})^2=7\tfrac{1}{4}$

23. $3\sqrt{70-\tfrac{1}{2}\tfrac{2}{}}=24$

24. $3(4\times5)=12\times15$

Practical Importance. Students of statistical method who are unfamiliar with the rules of computation often waste much time and energy and produce erroneous results because they are uncertain about the order in which arithmetic operations should be performed. Does $5\times6+24\div2$ equal 75, 27, 90, or 42? These four answers result from four different orders in which the work might be performed. To avoid confusion, mathematicians are agreed upon certain rules. These rules make 42 the correct answer.

EXPLANATION AND RULES

1. The order in which numbers are added does not affect the result. Thus $7+15+12=15+7+12=12+7+15$, etc. In general, $a+b+c=b+a+c=c+b+a$, etc.

2. The order in which numbers are multiplied does not affect the result. Thus $abc=bac=acb=bca=cab=cba$. It is sometimes more convenient to multiply in one order than in another. For example, $\tfrac{4}{9}\times\tfrac{6}{8}=4\times\tfrac{1}{9}\times6\times\tfrac{1}{8}=4\times\tfrac{1}{8}\times6\times\tfrac{1}{9}$ $=\tfrac{4}{8}\times\tfrac{6}{9}=\tfrac{1}{2}\times2\times\tfrac{1}{3}=\tfrac{2}{2}\times\tfrac{1}{3}=\tfrac{1}{3}$. This process is of course ordinarily abbreviated by the device of cancellation, but is given here in full to show the essential nature of the operations involved.

"Cancellation" is a term of ambiguous meaning which is rather carelessly used—sometimes to connote division, sometimes subtraction, sometimes merely "getting rid of." In general it is safer to avoid the use of this word and to go back to fundamental principles. "Cancellation" is the source of a large number of arithmetic errors made by persons who are not sure why they are cancelling.

3. In an example like $17+2\times10+64\div3-1$, the multiplication and division should be performed first, and then the addition and subtraction performed. Thus

$$17+2\times10+64\div3-1=17+20+21\tfrac{1}{3}-1=57\tfrac{1}{3}.$$

4. An expression enclosed in a parenthesis is to be treated as a single number. If convenient, the value of the parenthesis may be worked out first, as $3(27-2)=3(25)=75$. This is not always convenient, as in $35(\tfrac{1}{5}+\tfrac{1}{7})$, where it is easier to multiply each part of the parenthesis separately by the 35. In any case, the numbers within the parenthesis must all be treated in the same way.

5. The bar of a fraction has the same effect as a parenthesis, the numerator being treated as a single number and the denominator as a single number.

Thus, $\dfrac{3+12}{10+5}=\dfrac{15}{15}.$ This may also be written

$$(3+12)/(10+5)=15/15.$$

$$\frac{24-3}{4}=\frac{21}{4} \text{ and not } \frac{\overset{6}{\cancel{24}}-3}{4}=6-3.$$

Notice, however, that by rule (2), $\dfrac{5\times9}{2\times8}=5/2\times9/8$

$$=5/8\times9/2=\frac{5}{8}\times\frac{9}{2}.$$

Notice also that $\dfrac{4}{5}=\dfrac{3}{5}+\dfrac{1}{5}$, and that in general

$$\frac{a+b}{c}=\frac{a}{c}+\frac{b}{c}, \text{ hence } \frac{5+9}{2\times8}=\frac{5}{2\times8}+\frac{9}{2\times8}.$$

6. A radical sign has the same effect as a parenthesis, the expression under the radical sign being treated as a single number. Thus $\sqrt{64-4}=\sqrt{60}$ not $8-2$, and $\sqrt{1-(0.7)^2}$ $=\sqrt{1-0.49}=\sqrt{0.51}$.

EXERCISE 1

Perform the operations indicated below, writing your answers in the simplest possible form, and compare with the key.

1. $\dfrac{4}{7}\times\dfrac{25}{48}\times\dfrac{84}{15}$

2. $\dfrac{9}{8}\times\dfrac{42}{45}\times\dfrac{15}{12}$

3. $\dfrac{7\times22\times26}{39\times4\times10}$

4. $\dfrac{14}{75}\times\dfrac{39}{28}\times\dfrac{35}{26}$

5. $56\div2+6\times5-7$

6. $13+2\div5+6-4$

7. $28\div3+1$

8. $49\div\left(3+\dfrac{6}{5}\times\dfrac{10}{3}\right)+5$

9. $24(\tfrac{1}{3}+\tfrac{1}{4})$

10. $\dfrac{1}{4}\left(\dfrac{72}{5}+\dfrac{48}{7}\right)$

11. $(\tfrac{2}{5})^2$

12. $72\div(24\div2)$

13. $(\tfrac{1}{2})^2$

14. $15(1-\tfrac{2}{3})$

15. $\dfrac{5+3}{6+8}$

16. $\sqrt{1-(0.2)^2}$

17. $\sqrt{1-(0.3)^2}$

18. $\sqrt{1-(0.9)^2}$

SECOND TEST

Place a plus sign at the left of each statement which you believe to be true and a zero at the left of each statement which you believe to be false.

1. $9+6-2=6-2+9$

2. $48\div6+2=6$

3. $75(\tfrac{2}{3})=2(\tfrac{7.5}{3})$

4. $72\div2+4=12$

5. $5+63\div3=\tfrac{6\,8}{3}$

6. $(\tfrac{1}{3})^2=\tfrac{1}{9}$

7. $(\tfrac{3}{8})(\tfrac{1}{6})(\tfrac{4}{5})=(\tfrac{3}{8})(\tfrac{4}{6})(\tfrac{1}{5})$

8. $48\div(2\times3)=8$

9. $\tfrac{1}{8}(32+3)=4+3$

10. $\dfrac{9+2}{3}=3+2$

11. $\dfrac{(5+7)}{(2\times3)}=\dfrac{5}{2}+\dfrac{7}{3}$

12. $\dfrac{(5\times7)}{(2\times3)}=\dfrac{5}{2}\times\dfrac{7}{3}$

13. $\dfrac{(5+7)}{(2+3)}=\dfrac{5}{2}+\dfrac{7}{3}$

14. $\dfrac{(15\times4\times7)}{5}=3\times4\times7$

15. $\dfrac{(5\times6)}{4}=\dfrac{5}{4}\times\dfrac{6}{4}$

16. $\sqrt{36-25}=6-5$

17. $\tfrac{1}{8}(16-\tfrac{2}{3})=2-\tfrac{1}{12}$

18. $\sqrt{1-(0.3)^2}=\sqrt{0.7}$

19. $\dfrac{12+2}{3}=4\tfrac{2}{3}$

20. $\dfrac{48+5}{6}=8+5$

21. $\tfrac{1}{3}(6\times4)=2(\tfrac{4}{3})$

22. $4+(\tfrac{2}{3})(\tfrac{1}{2})=4\tfrac{1}{3}$

23. $2\sqrt{30+2\times3}=12$

24. $2(5\times3)=10\times6$

II

SIGNIFICANT FIGURES

Initial Test

After taking this test, compare your answers with the key in the back of the book. If you have made any errors, study the explanations and practice exercises and take the second test.

1. How many significant figures has each of the following numbers?

(1) 430091	(4) 0.00003	(7) 8000.
(2) 36.2	(5) 3.000	(8) 19000
(3) 0.00291	(6) 64.20	(9) 0.40

2. Round off each of the following numbers so that it contains 3 significant figures.

(1) 592641	(4) 5.6994	(7) 130.04
(2) 43.52	(5) 43350	(8) 3.9999
(3) 4.7251	(6) 53450	(9) 0.004625

3. Assume that all the numbers involved in the following computations are approximations and round off the results to the number of digits which you consider appropriate.

(1) $(2.315)^2 = 5.359225$

(2) $\sqrt{894} = 29.8998328$

(3) $\sqrt{237.9} = 15.424007$

(4) $(68.4)(4.6) = 314.64$

(5) $7362 \div 2.1 = 3505.71$

(6)
$$
\begin{array}{r}
2409.5 \\
13.6825 \\
2.421 \\
\hline
2425.6035
\end{array}
$$

Importance. "How many figures shall I retain in my answer?" is a question from which the statistical computer is never free. When a computing machine is used, it is so easy to carry computations to a large number of places

7

that there is a temptation to retain more digits in the final result than the study warrants. If a computer discards too many places, he throws away facts already at hand and creates a false impression that his figures are less reliable than they really are. If he retains too many places in his final result, he creates a false show of accuracy not justified by the precision of his original data.

Significant Figures. When a zero is used solely to fix the position of the decimal point, as in 0.003, it is not considered a significant digit. All other zeros, and all digits other than zero are significant. For example, in 0.00203, the first three zeros are mere padding, inserted for the sake of locating the decimal point and are consequently not significant. The zero standing between the 2 and the 3, however, has as much meaning as any other digit could have, and is significant. Consequently 0.00203 has three significant figures. In the number 2.30, the zero is significant because it is not used to fix the decimal point but to indicate that the third digit in the number is known to be 0. To drop off this last place and write the number as 2.3 would be to imply that we had only two-place accuracy instead of three-place.

Suppose that a line has been measured and found to be 9 meters long. If we write its length as 0.009 kilometers or as 9000 millimeters, we do not change the precision of the measurement. Each of these numbers has one significant digit and zeros which are used merely to locate the decimal point. However, the number 9000 itself gives us no information as to how many of its figures are significant. If we speak of a city of 9000 people, or the condition of the earth 9000 years ago, we are probably using numbers correct to one digit only. If we say that a man's salary is $9000 we are probably using a number correct to four places. To indicate that all four digits are significant, we may write 9000. with the decimal point printed. Sometimes a dot is printed above the last significant digit. Thus in 9000, we would understand that three digits are significant. It is obvious that the number of significant figures has nothing to do with the position of the decimal point.

68002 has 5 significant figures.
6.8002 has 5 significant figures.
0.600 has 3 significant figures.
40000. has 5 significant figures.
80000 has from 1 to 5 significant figures.

Numbers Obtained by Counting and by Measurement.
Numbers obtained by counting are exact. If we say there are 8 books on a table we mean exactly 8, not 8 and a fraction, or 7 and a fraction. Numbers obtained by measurement are approximate. Suppose that a boy has measured a rod and found it to be 8 cm. long. Probably this means "between $7\frac{1}{2}$ cm. and $8\frac{1}{2}$ cm." If he applies a finer instrument for measuring it, he may find its length to be, say 8.1 cm., which means "between 8.05 and 8.15 cm." Now he may take it to a laboratory and measure it with a micrometer which shows the length to be, say 8.093 cm. This means that the unit of precision is now 0.001 cm. and that the length of the rod is somewhere between 8.0925 cm. and 8.0935 cm. The measurement may be made as precise as human eyes and human instruments permit, and the limits of error may be rendered very narrow, but the measurement can never be made theoretically perfect.

The foregoing suggests that when we are dealing with the exact numbers which result from counting, it may be legitimate to carry computations as far as we wish. However, when the numbers with which we are dealing are approximations it is important that the final result of the computation be carried only so far as is appropriate to the precision of the original data. The number of figures which a computer sets down in his final result should be a sort of tacit pledge as to the amount of reliance which can be placed on the accuracy not only of his work but also of his data.

Illustrations of Inappropriate Procedure. 1. A man who wants an estimate of the diameter of a tree trunk passes a tapeline about it and finds the girth to be 68″. He divides this by 3.1416 and states that the diameter is 21.64502 in. It would have been more appropriate to say that the diameter is about 22 in. because (a) the circumference was correct to two places only and no measure based on that could be more accurate than the original measurement, and (b) the trunk was probably not exactly circular, and therefore the circumference not exactly π times the diameter. To use more than two figures in the result is misleading.

2. A high school principal computes to three decimal places the average grade of members of the senior class, stating these grades as 94.682, 91.427, 88.109, etc. When the well known inaccuracy of teachers' marks is taken into account, the pseudo-precision of these figures is almost laughable.

3. A statistical worker measures each of 36 persons in two traits and computes the coefficient of correlation between these traits as .3524. With so few cases and so low a correlation, not even the first figure is really reliable. If the investigation were repeated with another similar sample of 36 persons, there is about a fifty-fifty chance that the correlation coefficient would be somewhere between .25 and .45, and a fifty-fifty chance that it would be outside these limits. To write the result with four figures is inappropriate. If 10000 cases had been studied instead of 36, it would be appropriate to use three or four figures in the coefficient of correlation.

Number of Places to Be Retained in Computation with Approximate Numbers. We will use the phrase "the less accurate of two approximations" to mean the approximation written with the smaller number of significant figures, no matter where the decimal point comes. Thus 68 is to be considered less accurate than 68.1, 0.681, or 6810, and 0.004 is to be considered less accurate than 38, 3700, or 0.0037.

Rules

1. If the less accurate of two approximate numbers contains n significant digits, their product can be relied upon for n digits only, and should not be written with more.

Illustration:

$167 \times 4.352 = 727$, not 726.784, if both are approximate.

13% of $15943 = 2072.6$ if 13 is an exact number, and 15943 is approximate.

13% of $15943 = 2100$ if 13 is an approximation.

2. If the less accurate of two approximate numbers contains n significant digits, their quotient can be relied upon for n figures only and should not be written with more. This rule holds no matter which number is the divisor.

Illustration:

$3754 \div 18 = 208.5556$ if both numbers are exact.

$3754 \div 18 = 210$ if 18 is approximate.

$18 \div 3754 = 0.004794885$ if both are exact.

$18 \div 3754 = 0.004795$ if 18 is exact and 3754 approximate.

$18 \div 3754 = 0.0048$ if 18 is approximate.

3. If a number contains n significant digits, its square root can in general be relied upon for n digits.

Illustration: $\sqrt{435} = 20.856654$ if 435 is exact.

$\sqrt{435} = 20.9$ if 435 is approximate.

4. When several approximate numbers are to be added, the number of *decimal places* (not significant figures) in the result should be no greater than in the addend which has the smallest number of decimal places. A similar rule holds for subtraction.

Illustration:

$$435.2$$
$$13.689$$
$$5.12$$
$$\underline{18.4961}$$
$$472.5051$$

The sum should be rounded off to 472.5, since one of the addends is carried to the first decimal place only.

Note 1. When a computing machine is used, it is a satisfactory plan to carry intermediate computations out in full, and to round off the final result in accordance with these rules. When computations are performed with pencil it is satisfactory to carry each intermediate result two digits further than the rules would suggest, and to round off the final result in accordance with the rules.

Note 2. These rules do not cover the third illustration of inappropriate procedure given on page 10. That is a statistical rather than an arithmetical situation, and is treated in texts on statistical method.

Note 3. When a series of statistical results are published in one table, they should be carried out to a uniform number of decimal places, even if this requires the violation of some of the rules given above.

Note 4. Failing to record all the figures known to be accurate in a result is as inappropriate and misleading as retaining too many places.

Verification of the Rules. The reasonableness of the rules given above is readily illustrated. Let us consider the first illustration given under the first rule. The number 167 is an approximation for some number which is not less than 166.5 and not more than 167.5. The number 4.352 is an approximation for some number which is not less than 4.3515 and not more than 4.3525. Consequently their product is not less than

$$(166.5)(4.3515) = 724.52475$$

and is not more than

$$(167.5)(4.3525) = 729.04375.$$

Since these two results do not agree in the third place, it is certainly not reasonable to state the result with more than three significant digits. Similarly

$$\sqrt{435} \text{ is not less than } \sqrt{434.5} = 20.84466$$

and $\sqrt{435}$ is not greater than $\sqrt{435.5} = 20.86864.$

Here the results agree for the first three places, and we can be confident that the first three places are correct.

Rounding Off a Number. When the first of the digits to be dropped is less than 5, the digits are dropped with no change in the preceding digit. When the digit or digits to be dropped are greater than an exact 5 (*i.e.*, the first digit is 6, 7, 8, or 9, or the first digit is a 5 followed by other digits not zero), the preceding digit should be increased by 1. When the digit to be dropped is a 5 followed only by zeros, it is customary to make the preceding digit even.

While this last practice is arbitrary, the reason for it is clear. If 423500 is an approximate number which we wish to round to three significant figures, we are handicapped by not knowing whether the true value of the number is less than 423500, in which case we should round it to 423000, or more than 423500, in which case we should round it to 424000. If the true value were 423499, the rounded value should be 423000. If the true value were 423501, the rounded value should be 424000. If in all such cases we agreed to increase the preceding digit, in the course of a long problem we should get a cumulative error in excess. If in all such cases we agreed to drop the 5 with no change in the preceding digit, in the course of a long problem we should get a cumulative error in defect. Consequently the rule provides for alternating practice to avoid a cumulative error.

Illustrations:

Number	Number Rounded to 4 Significant Figures
715.349	715.3
715.351	715.4
499.984	500.0
12.4350	12.44
436850	436800
52996.1	53000

Note. If a number is rounded off first to 6 places, then to 5, then to 4, etc., inconsistencies may arise, and therefore such successive rounding should be avoided.

EXERCISE 2

1. Place a cross in front of each of the following which you consider to be an exact number, and a circle in front of each of those which you consider to be an approximate number.
   (1) The number of patients receiving treatment at a clinic on a particular day.
   (2) The number of square feet in the floor space of an auditorium.
   (3) The number of calories in a piece of apple pie.
   (4) The height in inches of a person.
   (5) The age in days of a child.
   (6) The number of windows in a school building.
   (7) The number of children on a playground.
   (8) The reading of the government thermometer at a given place on a given day and hour.

2. How many significant figures has each of the following numbers?

(1) 0.0029   (5) 0.020   (9) 3000
(2) 1.0029   (6) 30.0   (10) 450
(3) 46821   (7) 45062   (11) 0.0301
(4) 90063   (8) 0.012   (12) 3.60

3. Round off each of the following numbers so that it contains four significant figures.

(1) 5689243   (5) 99.0000   (9) 5.34651
(2) 437550   (6) 2.5685   (10) 3.00012
(3) 0.01234   (7) 5.34350   (11) 488967
(4) 28.99750   (8) 5.34650   (12) 32105

4. Assume that all of the numbers involved in the following computations are approximations and round off the result of the computation to the number of digits which you consider appropriate for a final result.

(1) $(41.3)^2 = 1705.69$

(2) $(4.13)^2 = 17.0569$

(3) $\sqrt{4.13} = 2.03224$

(4) $\sqrt{62.79} = 7.9240141$

(5) $\sqrt{24} = 4.8989795$

(6) $\tfrac{2}{3} = 0.66666667$

(7) $3.3 \div 86 = 0.03837209$

(8) $\dfrac{15}{8441} = 0.001777041$

(9) $(3.1416)(24) = 75.3984$

(10) $(5.26873)(16) = 84.29968$

(11)   3245.5
       163.27
         2.468
        13.3
     ─────────
     3424.538

(12)   6.375
      12.5
       3.29
     ────────
     22.165

5. If 75 is understood to be an exact number and all the other numbers in these computations are understood to be approximations, to how many places would it be appropriate to carry each of the following computations?

(1) $\sqrt{75}$ (6) $(75)^3$
(2) $(75)(46.24)$ (7) $(75)(4.923)(36)$
(3) $75 \div 321$ (8) $75 \div 1346$
(4) $52 \div 75$ (9) $417 \div 75$
(5) $(75)^2$ (10) $(75)(13.57) \div 3.6$

SECOND TEST

1. How many significant figures has each of the following numbers?

(1) 53062	(4) 0.0002	(7) 15000.
(2) 14.05	(5) 6.00	(8) 2000
(3) 0.0037	(6) 73.10	(9) 0.30

2. Round off each of the following numbers so that it contains 3 significant figures.

(1) 23.750	(4) 36.252	(7) 0.0004231
(2) 1.3650	(5) 78.249	(8) 89963
(3) 27992	(6) 21003	(9) 1.3851

3. Assume that all the numbers involved in the following computations are approximations and round off the results to the number of digits you think appropriate.

(1) $(7.26)^2 = 52.7076$

(2) $\sqrt{5651} = 75.173134$

(3) $\sqrt{416.3} = 20.40343$

(4) $(7.326)(1.2) = 8.7912$

(5) $9.2463 \div 25 = 0.369852$

(6)
$$
\begin{array}{r}
4500.375 \\
2.15 \\
73.6 \\
4.823 \\
\hline
4580.948
\end{array}
$$

III

SQUARE ROOT

Initial Test

Find the square roots of the following numbers, carrying results correct to 4 significant figures. Compare your answers with those in the key. If you make any errors, study the rules and practice material and take the second test.

1. 4972.36
2. 425.4
3. 0.002019
4. 0.0863
5. 56.12

6. 4000
7. 0.9
8. 6.4
9. 360
10. 0.1

Practical Importance. In computing a standard deviation or a correlation coefficient it is necessary to extract square root, so that almost from the beginning the student finds that a large proportion of statistical problems involve square root. When available, computing machines or tables of square roots are used, but there are many occasions when no mechanical help is at hand and then square root must be found by arithmetical methods.

This section may be omitted by those students who expect always to have at hand either tables of squares and square roots or a computing machine. The use of such tables is discussed in Chapter IV and the use of logarithms in extracting roots is treated in Chapter XVIII.

Rules and Illustration

$$\sqrt{631.425} = ?$$

1. Point off the number into periods of 2 places each, *beginning at the decimal point.*

$$\overline{63}\,\overline{1}.\overline{42}\,\overline{50}$$

2. Find the largest square in the left hand period.

     4

3. Subtract this square from the left hand period and enter its square root as the first digit in the root of the number.

$$\frac{2}{\overline{6}\overline{3}\overline{1}.\overline{4}\overline{2}\overline{5}\overline{0}}$$
$$\frac{4}{2}$$

4. Bring down the next period (next two digits) forming a partial remainder.

$$\frac{2}{\overline{6}\overline{3}\overline{1}.\overline{4}\overline{2}\overline{5}\overline{0}}$$
$$\frac{4}{231}$$

5. Double the root already found to serve as a trial divisor.

$$2 \times 2 = 4$$

6. Temporarily dropping the right hand digit in the partial remainder, divide the rest of the partial remainder by the trial divisor to give a trial quotient.

$$\frac{23}{4} = 5$$

7. Write this trial quotient as a new digit in the root and also as the last digit in the completed divisor.

$$\frac{2\ 5}{\overline{6}\overline{3}\overline{1}.\overline{4}\overline{2}\overline{5}\overline{0}}$$
$$\frac{4}{}$$
$$45 \ \overline{\big)\ 231}$$

8. Multiply the completed divisor by the trial quotient.

$$45 \times 5 = 225$$

9. Subtract this product from the partial remainder.

$$\frac{2\ 5\ .}{\overline{6}\overline{3}\overline{1}.\overline{4}\overline{2}\overline{5}\overline{0}}$$
$$\frac{4}{}$$
$$45 \ \overline{\big)\ 231}$$
$$5 \ \overline{\big)\ 225}$$
$$6$$

10. Repeat steps 4 to 9 as often as necessary.

11. Place the decimal point in its proper place. Counting from the decimal point, there should be *one digit* in the root corresponding to *each period* in the number. When the work is set down in the fashion illustrated here, the decimal point in the root is placed directly above the decimal point in the number, and each digit in the root is written above the corresponding period in the number.

12. See the discussion of special cases in the practice material.

Complete Solution

$$2\ 5\ .\ 1\ 2\ 8$$
$$\overline{6\ 3\ 1.4\ 2\ 5\ 0\ 0\ 0}$$

	4
4 5	2 3 1
	2 2 5
5 0 1	6 4 2
	5 0 1
5 0 2 2	1 4 1 5 0
	1 0 0 4 4
5 0 2 4 8	4 1 0 6 0 0
	4 0 1 9 8 4
	8 6 1 6

Second Illustration

$$5\ 3\ 3\ .\ 7\ 2\ 8$$
$$\overline{2\ 8\ 4\ 8\ 6\ 5.5\ 9\ 9\ 7\ 0\ 0}$$

	2 5
1 0 3	3 4 8
	3 0 9
1 0 6 3	3 9 6 5
	3 1 8 9
1 0 6 6 7	7 7 6 5 9
	7 4 6 6 9
1 0 6 7 4 2	2 9 9 0 9 7
	2 1 3 4 8 4
1 0 6 7 4 4 8	8 5 6 1 3 0 0
	8 5 3 9 5 8 4
	2 1 7 1 6

EXERCISE 3

1. Point into periods and compare with answers in key.

(1) 437	(6) 12.53751	(11) 0.35
(2) 4370	(7) 136.4	(12) 0.4
(3) 4.37	(8) 0.00009	(13) 3.214
(4) 0.437	(9) 90.123	(14) 0.002
(5) 0.000437	(10) 567.2	(15) 0.1

2. State by inspection the first significant digit in the square root of each of the numbers in Question 1.

3. State by inspection the first significant digit in the square root of each of the following numbers.

(1) 640	(5) 0.09	(9) 6250	(13) 0.81
(2) 3.60	(6) 90	(10) 490	(14) 0.225
(3) 0.1	(7) 400	(11) 250	(15) 371.436
(4) 8.1	(8) 40	(12) 0.04	(16) 5297.31

4. Practice extracting the square roots of the following numbers until you are sure of the general procedure before going on to the special cases discussed under **5** and **6** below.

(1) 4827	(4) 969.5	(7) 0.3049
(2) 1399	(5) 1708	(8) 823.69
(3) 2648	(6) 19.61	(9) 55696

5. Sometimes the trial divisor found in step **5** is larger than the part of the partial remainder into which it is to be divided (step **6**). Then a zero must be entered in the root, another period is brought down, and the work proceeds as before through steps **5** to **9**.

Illustration:

$$
\begin{array}{r}
2\ 0\ 4\ .\ 0\ 4\ 1 \\
\hline
4\,1\,6\,3\,3\,.\,0\,0\,0\,0\,0\,0 \\
4
\end{array}
$$

$$
\begin{array}{r|l}
4\,0\,4 & 1\,6\,3\,3 \\
& 1\,6\,1\,6 \\
4\,0\,8\,0\,4 & 1\,7\,0\,0\,0\,0 \\
& 1\,6\,3\,2\,1\,6 \\
4\,0\,8\,0\,8\,1 & 6\,7\,8\,4\,0\,0
\end{array}
$$

Extract the square roots of the following numbers:

(1) 93086	(3) 36.6025	(5) 81.92	(7) 4.2849
(2) 2516	(4) 4988.6	(6) 226.50	(8) 6497.97

6. Sometimes the product found in step **8** proves to be larger than the partial remainder from which it is to be subtracted. Then it is necessary to decrease the trial quotient by one point, and to retrace steps **7** and **8**. After a little practice, the computer can anticipate this situation and use the smaller quotient in the first place.

Illustration:

$$
\begin{array}{r}
8\ \ 6 \\
\hline
7\,3\,8\,6 \\
6\,4 \\
\end{array}
$$

$$
1\,6\,6\ \Big|\ \begin{array}{l} 9\,8\,6 \\ 9\,9\,6 \end{array}
$$

Evidently 6 is too large so we must change it to 5. An experienced computer would have foreseen this and would not have attempted to use the 6.

$$
\begin{array}{r}
8\ \ 5\ .9 \\
\hline
7\,3\,8\,6\,. \\
6\,4 \\
\end{array}
$$

$$
1\,6\,5\ \Big|\ \begin{array}{l} 9\,8\,6 \\ 8\,2\,5 \end{array}
$$

$$
1\,7\,0\,9\ \Big|\ \begin{array}{l} 1\,6\,1\,0\,0 \\ 1\,5\,3\,8\,1 \end{array}
$$

Extract the square roots of the following numbers:

(1) 77953	(4) 194.88	(7) 930.86
(2) 59.1515	(5) 48224	(8) 73062.29
(3) 2.5408	(6) 10.2272	(9) 14.50842

Approximation Method. A method of using division to find successive approximations to the square root of a number is very useful when a computing machine is used, and some persons like it for pencil and paper work. The following example illustrates the procedure.

$$\sqrt{284865.1997} = ?$$

(1) Estimate the square root mentally.   500

(2) Divide the number by this estimate.

$$\frac{284865.1997}{500} = 569.73$$

(3) Take the average between the divisor and quotient. The result is a better approximation to the root than either divisor or quotient.

$$\frac{500+569.73}{2}=534.86$$

(4) Repeat steps (2) and (3) as often as necessary to secure desired precision in the answer.

$$\frac{284865.1997}{534.9}=532.6$$

$$\frac{534.9+532.6}{2}=533.75$$

etc.

When the divisor and the quotient are in agreement for n digits, the root will be correct for at least n digits, and probably for more than n.

SECOND TEST

Extract the square roots of the following numbers, carrying results correct to 4 significant figures.

(1) 3841.25		(6) 9000
(2) 927.2		(7) 0.1
(3) 0.002106		(8) 3.6
(4) 0.07213		(9) 710.0
(5) 35.72		(10) 0.4

IV

READING A SQUARE ROOT FROM A TABLE

INITIAL TEST

On page 25 is a section of a table of squares and square roots. Read all answers from this table as accurately as possible. Do not extract any root or square any number by ordinary arithmetic processes. If a question calls for a square root which cannot be read from the table, make a cross in the space left for the answer. Compare your answers with the key in the back of the book. If you have errors, study the explanations and practice exercises.

1. Read the square root of each of the following numbers from the table as accurately as possible without interpolation. If no root can be obtained from the table, make a cross in place of the answer.

   (1) 65800   (3) 0.087   (5) 6.889
   (2) 65.61   (4) 4251   (6) 0.004343

2. Read the square of each of the following numbers from the table as accurately as possible without interpolation.

   (1) 25.65   (2) 0.09328

3. Interpolate in the table to find the square root of the following:

   (1) 65650   (2) 65.82

4. Interpolate in the table to find the square of the following:

   (1) 6583   (2) 8.44

Practical Importance. A competent statistical worker arranges his work so as to make the largest possible use of mechanical aids. If he has access to a computing machine

or a table of squares he almost never extracts square root
by the use of pencil and paper. The other methods are
much quicker and afford less chance for error. Reading
square root from a table is an easy process, yet even here
the novice is likely to make certain typical mistakes.

Reading the Table Directly. Table I gives us a number
in the column headed N, its square in the column headed N^2
and its square root in the column headed $\sqrt{N}$. Thus if we
want to know the square root of 656 we may look for 656 in
the N column, and opposite this, in the $\sqrt{N}$ column we
will find its square root which is 25.6125. Or again, suppose
we want the square root of 87. We will locate 87 in
the first column, and look for the corresponding number in
the column headed $\sqrt{N}$. Here we find 9.3274, which is the
square root of 87.

Reading the Table Indirectly. Reading the table directly
we find that the square of 81 is 6561. Now if 6561 is the
square of 81, then of course 81 is the square root of 6561.
That is, if $81^2 = 6561$, then $81 = \sqrt{6561}$. If we locate these
numbers in the table, we see that we have found 6561 in
the N^2 column and 81 in the N column. Thus to find a
square root it is often more convenient to locate in the N^2
column the number whose root is to be taken and to read
the root in the N column. This often gives us a more accurate answer than to read the table directly. As another
example, find the square root of 430340. In the N^2 column
we find 430336, and opposite it in the N column we find 656.
This tells us that the root of 430336 is 656. It is obvious
that the root of 430340 is a little larger than the root of
430336 but it is also clear that it is much nearer to 656
than to 657. Hence 656 is the square root of 430340 correct
to three places.

To emphasize this alternative method until you are familiar with it, write X above the N^2 column, and $\sqrt{X}$ above

TABLE I

PORTIONS OF A TABLE OF SQUARES AND SQUARE ROOTS

Number	Square		Square Root	
N	N²	Δ	√N	Δ
650	422500		25.4951	
		1301		196
651	423801		25.5147	
		1303		196
652	425104		25.5343	
		1305		196
653	426409		25.5539	
		1307		195
654	427716		25.5734	
		1309		196
655	429025		25.5930	
		1311		195
656	430336		25.6125	
		1313		195
657	431649		25.6320	
		1315		195
658	432964		25.6515	
		1317		195
659	434281		25.6710	
80	6400		8.9443	
		161		557
81	6561		9.0000	
		163		554
82	6724		9.0554	
		165		550
83	6889		9.1104	
		167		548
84	7056		9.1652	
		169		543
85	7225		9.2195	
		171		541
86	7396		9.2736	
		173		538
87	7569		9.3274	
		175		534
88	7744		9.3808	
		177		532
89	7921		9.4340	

the N column. To show still another relationship, write Y beside the $\sqrt{N}$ and Y^2 beside N, thus:

Number	Square	Square Root
N	N^2	$\sqrt{N}$
$\sqrt{X}$	X	$\sqrt[4]{X}$
Y^2	Y^4	Y

When a problem calls for the square root of a number, we can either look for that number in the column N and find its root under $\sqrt{N}$, or we can look for the number under X and find its root under $\sqrt{X}$, as is convenient. To square a number, we can either look for the number under N and its square under N^2, or for the number under Y and its square under Y^2.

Placing the Decimal Point. When a number is multiplied by 10, its square is multiplied by 100. When a number is divided by 10, its square is divided by 100. Symbolically we may write $(10a)^2 = 100a^2$ and $\left(\dfrac{a}{10}\right)^2 = \dfrac{a^2}{100}$. Therefore if the decimal point is moved *one* place to the right (or left) in the number, it will be moved *two* places to the right (or left) in the square.

Illustration:

$$
\begin{aligned}
(651)^2 &= 423801 \\
(65.1)^2 &= 4238.01 \\
(6.51)^2 &= 42.3801 \\
(0.651)^2 &= 0.423801 \text{ etc.}
\end{aligned}
$$

Notice that the numbers 4.23801, 423.801, and 0.0423801 do not appear in this table at all. In general, no square with an odd number of digits to the left of the decimal point or an odd number of zeros to the right of the point will be found in this set, no matter how far it should be extended.

Such numbers belong to an entirely different set, not included in the small table on page 25. Such a set would include:

$$(205.86)^2 \quad = 42378.3396$$
$$(20.586)^2 \quad = \quad 423.783396$$
$$(2.0586)^2 \quad = \qquad 4.23783396$$
$$(0.20586)^2 = \qquad 0.0423783396 \text{ etc.}$$

If we were trying to read from the tables the square root of a number whose first five digits were 4, 2, 3, 7, and 8, it is clear that we should need to know the position of the decimal point before we could find even the first digit of the root.

Rule. To find the square root of a number from a table first point off the number into periods of two places beginning at the decimal point. Then take either step (A) or step (B), as is convenient.

    (A) Look for the number in the column headed N and find the root in the column headed $\sqrt{N}$.

    (B) Look for the number in the column headed N^2 and find the root in the column headed N.

When the sequence of digits for the root has been thus determined, place the decimal point in such a way that, *beginning at the point*, there shall be one digit in the root for every period in the number.

Caution. Care must be used to see that the decimal point in the number read from the table is in the same position as in the number whose root is to be found, or that its position differs by an *even* number of places. Thus, if the table shows 368 in the column of squares, we can obtain the square roots of 3.68, or 0.0368, or 3680000, but not of 36.8, 3680, or 0.368. The majority of the mistakes made by the novice in reading square roots from a table probably relate to the decimal point.

EXERCISE 4

For each of the following numbers, determine the first digit of the root by inspection, and fill in zeros to locate the decimal point. This will give a rough approximation to the root. Do not try to find a more exact value.

Illustration:

$$\sqrt{37241} = 100, \qquad \sqrt{0.0005} = 0.02, \qquad \sqrt{0.012} = 0.1, \qquad \sqrt{7563} = 80.$$

1. 528631	**9.** 0.4	**17.** 0.004
2. 7961	**10.** 0.001	**18.** 0.09
3. 10520	**11.** 160	**19.** 0.009
4. 3674200	**12.** 4400	**20.** 651.2
5. 920.01	**13.** 250	**21.** 9000
6. 19.3	**14.** 12.39	**22.** 0.025
7. 3940	**15.** 0.1	**23.** 8.1
8. 0.053	**16.** 1.03	**24.** 49632

Interpolation. Suppose that we wish to get from the table on page 25 the approximate value of $(82.7)^2$. Obviously this value lies between $(82)^2 = 6724$ and $(83)^2 = 6889$, and lies nearer to the latter. How much nearer? If we think of a scale running from 82.0 to 83.0, we see that 82.7 is located at a point which is $\frac{7}{10}$ of the distance from 82.0 to 83.0. We may then assume that its square will be approximately $\frac{7}{10}$ of the way from $(82)^2 = 6724$ to $(83)^2 = 6889$. The difference between these two squares is $6889 - 6724 = 165$, and $\frac{7}{10}$ of the difference is 115.5. $6724 + \frac{7}{10}(165) = 6839.5$ or the approximate value of $(82.7)^2$. The actual value of $(82.7)^2 = 6839.29$, and we see that our interpolated value has as many digits correct as there are significant figures in 82.7, which is all that can be legitimately expected.

Suppose that from the table we wish to find the approximate value of the square root of 7280. By inspection of Table I we obtain the following:

Scale of Numbers	Scale of Squares
83.0 –	6889
82.9 –	

$$86^2 = 7396$$
$$(?)^2 = 7280$$
$$(85)^2 = 7225$$

The difference $(86)^2 - (85)^2 = 7396 - 7225 = 171$. Note that the size of this difference may be read immediately from the column marked Δ. Now the square in which we are interested stands at a point which is $\frac{55}{171}$ of the way from $(85)^2$ to $(86)^2$ and therefore its root should be approximately $\frac{55}{171}$ of the way from 85 to 86. Now $\frac{55}{171}$ of $1 = 0.3$, and the approximate root is therefore 85.3.

Such interpolation is called *linear interpolation*. It assumes that a good approximation is afforded by treating the numbers and their squares as though they were proportional to each other, as though a graph of the squares would be a straight line. Now we know this is not true in general, but for any *small section* of its course the graph is so nearly straight that no great inaccuracy results from treating it as though it were straight. (For work which requires greater precision, more exact methods of interpolation are possible.) Because this method gives only a *first approximation* to the true result, one should not try to interpolate more than one additional figure in the root, and should not carry the square out to more places than are already given.

The columns marked Δ are columns of differences between

Scale column values:
82.8 –
82.7 –   ?
82.6 –
82.5 –
82.4 –
82.3 –
82.2 –
82.1 –
82.0 –   6724

tabular entries to facilitate the interpolation. (Δ, or delta, is the capital letter D in the Greek alphabet, and is used often to stand for "difference.") These differences are not always printed since they can be readily found by subtraction.

EXERCISE 5

1. Find the square root of 656.35
Procedure:

Number	Root
657	25.6320
656.35	?
656	25.6125
	0.0195

$25.6125 + (0.35)(0.0195) = 25.6193$ *Ans.*

2. Find the square root of 87.14
Procedure:

Number	Root
88	9.3808
87	9.3274
	0.0534

$9.3274 + (0.14)(0.0534) = 9.3349$ *Ans.*

3. Find the square root of 4305
Procedure:

Number	Root
4316.49	65.7
4303.36	65.6
13.13	

$(4305 - 4303.36) \div (4316.49 - 4303.36) = 0.125$
$65.6 + (0.125)(0.1) = 65.61$ *Ans.*

4. Find the square root of each of the following:

(1) 78.02	(4) 6.524	(7) 8570
(2) 65	(5) 4300	(8) 6.562
(3) 0.6581	(6) 7500	(9) 0.065

5. Find the square of each of the following:

(1) 6575	(2) 9.235	(3) 0.06584

SECOND TEST

1. Read the square root of each of the following numbers from the table on page 25 as accurately as possible without interpolation. If no root can be obtained from the table, make a cross in place of the answer.

   (1) 0.0657   (3) 65.3   (5) 0.0655
   (2) 4.316   (4) 0.007056   (6) 7.744

2. Read the square of each of the following numbers from the table as accurately as possible without interpolation.
   (1) 0.894   (2) 2.552

3. Interpolate in the table to find the square root of the following:
   (1) 8370   (2) 42.50

4. Interpolate in the table to find the square of the following:
   (1) 6.543   (2) 0.934

V

PLACING A DECIMAL POINT

Initial Test

In each of the following problems, select the answer which is the best value for the computation indicated at the left. Do not perform the computation, but select the best answer by inspection. You may assume that one of the four given answers is correct. Write the number of the correct answer on the line at the right, as in Question 1.

		1	2	3	4	
1.	$(.06)(4.25)$	$=25.5$	2.55	0.255	0.0255	3
2.	$(0.05) \div (0.001)$	$=5$	50	0.5	.0005	——
3.	$(4.31)(6.15)$	$=2.65$	26.5	265	2650	——
4.	$(0.326) \div (.02)$	$=16.3$	1.63	0.163	0.0163	——
5.	$\dfrac{(0.04)(.08)}{.02}$	$=.16$	.016	.0016	.00016	——
6.	$(0.07)^2$	$=4.9$	0.49	0.049	0.0049	——
7.	$(0.1)^2$	$=1.0$	0.1	0.01	0.001	——
8.	$\sqrt{360}$	$=6$	60	18.9	1.89	——
9.	$\sqrt{0.0049}$	$=0.7$	0.07	0.007	0.022	——
10.	$\sqrt{1-(.2)^2}$	$=0.98$	0.96	0.80	0.60	——
11.	$\sqrt{1.6}$	$=4$	0.4	12.6	1.26	——
12.	$\sqrt{0.0144}$	$=0.12$	0.38	0.012	0.038	——
13.	$\sqrt{0.000004}$	$=0.02$	.002	0.063	0.0063	——
14.	0.01	$=.01\%$	.1	.001	.01	——
15.	$.0012$	$=12\%$	1.2%	0.12%	.0012%	——
16.	0.031	$=31\%$	3.1%	.31%	.031%	——
17.	$(32)(.4500)$	$=144$	1440	14.4%	1440%	——

32

Practical Importance. A great many errors in statistical calculations are due to a mistake in placing a decimal point. People who expect to do any considerable amount of computation should be able to place a decimal point with the same sort of automatic precision as that with which an expert chauffeur changes gears. Otherwise many hours of time may be wasted in rectifying erroneous work.

Multiplication. In multiplying decimals, multiply as with whole numbers; then, beginning at the right, point off as many decimal places in the product as there are in the multiplier and the multiplicand together.

In practice it is often preferable not to carry out the complete multiplication, because we do not need an answer with so many decimal places in it. Then we estimate the size of the answer by multiplying the leading digits in the two numbers. Study these illustrations to see how the position of the decimal point could be found without performing the complete multiplication. Only the first three digits in each answer have been given.

Example	*Product of Leading Digits*	*Answer*
$(0.0372)(0.0913) = ?$	$(0.04)(0.09) = 0.0036$	0.00340
$(93.25)(0.000241) = ?$	$(90)(0.0002) = 0.018$	0.0225

Division. In dividing by a decimal, count as many places to the right of the decimal point in the dividend as there are decimal places in the divisor and place the decimal point in the quotient directly over this point. Be careful always to align your quotient figure with the corresponding figure in the dividend, as shown in this example.

$$6.32\overline{)2.93\overset{0.464}{6}1}$$

$$\begin{array}{r} 0.4\,6\,4 \\ 6.32\overline{)2.9\,3\,6\,1} \\ 2\,5\,2\,8 \\ \hline 4\,0\,8\,1 \\ 3\,7\,9\,2 \\ \hline 2\,8\,9\,0 \end{array}$$

In practice it is useful to be able to estimate the approximate size of a quotient by finding the quotient of the leading digits. In the illustration given, we would see that the quotient of 2.9361 by 6.32 is in the neighborhood of 3 divided by 6, and is therefore somewhere near 0.5.

Example	Approximate Quotient of Leading Digits	Quotient
72.41 ÷ 263	70 ÷ 300 = 0.2	0.275
0.0523 ÷ 0.064	0.05 ÷ 0.06 = 0.8	0.817
2793 ÷ 0.081	3000 ÷ 0.08 = 40000	34481

Square Root. Study the rules, explanations and practice exercises in the section on square root, pages 17 to 21.

Zero before the Decimal Point. Printing a zero to the left of the decimal point when no other digit is there, is an excellent practice because it guards against having the decimal point overlooked. It would be possible to mistake .12 for 12, but scarcely possible so to mistake 0.12. A zero in this position has obviously no effect upon the size of the number, and .12 = 0.12.

Zero to the Right of a Decimal Fraction. In computing, a zero or zeros at the right of a decimal fraction should be dropped. To multiply by 3.6200, multiply by 3.62. To divide by 0.31000, divide by 0.31. Such zeros have no meaning for the computation, and to carry them is a waste of time and a prolific source of error. Such zeros, when properly used, furnish important information concerning the degree of precision of measurement, as was stated in Chapter II, and for this reason it may be desirable to restore them *at the end of the process*, but during the computation they should be ignored.

Multiplication or Division by a Power of Ten. To multiply by 10 we merely set the decimal point one place to the right, to multiply by 100, two places, by 1000, three places, and so on. To divide by these numbers we move the decimal a corresponding number of places to the left. Consequently to multiply or divide by a number ending in one or more zeros. we do not set down the zeros in our computation, but move the decimal point in the answer one place to the right for every zero if we are multiplying, one place to the left for every zero if we are dividing.

Per Cents. Since 16% means "16 per hundred" it is equal to $\frac{16}{100}$ or 0.16. This is a very simple relationship, yet many mistakes are made in changing from the per cent notation to the decimal notation and vice versa. Study the following:

$$0.015 = 1.5\% \qquad\qquad 0.0004 = 0.04\%$$
$$0.360 = 36\% \qquad\qquad 0.0126 = 1.26\%$$
$$0.02 \ = \ 2\% \qquad\qquad 2.40 \ \ = 240\%$$
$$1.12 \ = 112\% \qquad\qquad 0.093 \ = \ 9.3\%$$

Estimating the Size of a Result. The best safeguard against errors in placing of decimal points is the habit of estimating in advance about how large the result of a computation should be. The following examples worked out in considerable detail illustrate ways in which this can be done. After a little practice, one should learn to carry out these approximations with such facility as to be unaware of the steps, seeming to recognize the results almost immediately.

Example 1. In division it is often helpful to move the decimal points in dividend and divisor the same number of places to the right or left.

   $0.048 \div 0.0079 = 48 \div 7.9$ or roughly $48 \div 8$. The quotient is approximately 6.

   $5234 \div 61.24 = 523.4 \div 6.124$ or roughly $500 \div 6$. The quotient is a little more than 80.

Example 2. Attention may be centered on the leading digits, zeros being substituted for the other digits, and an approximate value obtained which gives the position of the decimal point.

7734×415 is roughly 8000×400=3200000.

38.25×192.3 is a little less than 40×200, which is 8000.

563.2×0.0382 is a little less than 600×0.04, which is the same as 6.00×4 or 24.

Exercise 6

1. What per cent is equivalent to each of the following?

(1) 0.052	(6) 0.013	(11) 0.0006	(16) 2.162
(2) 0.175	(7) 0.507	(12) 0.2014	(17) 0.005
(3) 0.240	(8) 1.423	(13) 0.3200	(18) 3.013
(4) 1.020	(9) 0.091	(14) 0.0051	(19) 0.942
(5) 0.503	(10) 0.003	(15) 0.0603	(20) 0.863

2. Change each of the following to a per cent.

(1) $\dfrac{0.04}{0.05}$ (6) $\dfrac{420}{35000}$ (11) $\dfrac{2.8}{25}$

(2) $\dfrac{3.6}{4.8}$ (7) $\dfrac{170}{1000}$ (12) $\dfrac{63}{70}$

(3) $\dfrac{0.06}{7.5}$ (8) $\dfrac{465}{10000}$ (13) $\dfrac{240}{4800}$

(4) $\dfrac{0.008}{0.24}$ (9) $\dfrac{143}{2000}$ (14) $\dfrac{0.01}{0.5}$

(5) $\dfrac{0.35}{0.14}$ (10) $\dfrac{65}{100}$ (15) $\dfrac{0.06}{0.8}$

3. Find mentally the first digit or first two digits in the answer for each of the following exercises, and place the decimal point in the appropriate place, filling in with zeros where necessary. It is the position of the decimal point in which we are interested now, rather than the size of the digit in the answer. In the first question, for example, 210,000, 240,000, or 200,000 would be considered a satisfactory answer. When you compare your answers with the key, count an answer right if the decimal point is correctly placed.

(1) 7814×31.52

(2) 5.23×10.41

(3) 0.27×0.0062

(4) $0.32 \div 0.004$

(5) $42.9 \div 0.07$

(6) $0.024 \div 0.04$

(7) $(0.03)^2$

(8) $(41.2)^2$

(9) $\sqrt{360000}$

(10) $\sqrt{85241}$

(11) $\sqrt{0.003}$

(12) $\sqrt{0.0005}$

(13) $\sqrt{741.23}$

(14) $\sqrt{0.06}$

(15) $\sqrt{\dfrac{491}{53}}$

(16) $\sqrt{\dfrac{9.41}{46}}$

(17) $\sqrt{\dfrac{4325}{137}}$

(18) $\sqrt{\dfrac{7153}{2.71}}$

(19) $\sqrt{\dfrac{885}{0.02}}$

(20) $\sqrt{\dfrac{0.0137}{50}}$

4. In each of the following, select the value which is the best answer for the computation indicated at the left. Do not perform the computation, but select the best answer by inspection. Write the number of the correct answer on the line at the right.

		1	*2*	*3*	*4*	
(1)	$(463)(0.10)$ =	463	46.3	4.63	4630	——
(2)	$(0.030)(0.2)$ =	0.6	0.06	0.006	0.0006	——
(3)	$3(7.500)$ =	22.5	225	2.25	0.225	——
(4)	$(5.3)(1.2)$ =	6.36	636	63.60	0.636	——
(5)	$.12 \div .0002$ =	.06	600	.0006	.000006	——
(6)	$(0.1)^2$ =	0.1	0.01	0.001	0.0001	——
(7)	$0.34 \div 12$ =	2.8	0.28	0.028	0.0028	——
(8)	0.042 =	4.2%	42%	0.42%	0.042%	——
(9)	0.0092 =	92%	9.2%	0.92%	0.0092%	——
(10)	$43.2 \div 2.4$ =	18	1.8	180	1800	——
(11)	$(0.05)^2$ =	0.25	0.05	0.025	0.0025	——
(12)	$\sqrt{365}$ =	6.0	60	191	19.1	——
(13)	$\sqrt{\dfrac{1}{8}}$ =	2.83	3.54	0.112	0.354	——
(14)	$\sqrt{0.01}$ =	0.1	.01	0.001	0.0001	——

		1	2	3	4	
(15)	$\sqrt{1-(.5)^2}$	=0.7	0.5	0.75	0.866	——
(16)	$\sqrt{0.00004}$	=0.06	.002	0.006	0.0002	——
(17)	$\sqrt{8.1}$	=9	0.9	2.8	0.28	——
(18)	$\sqrt{17403}$	=417	41.7	13.2	132	——
(19)	$48 \div 6000$	=0.8	0.08	0.008	8000	——
(20)	$4.8 \div 60.00$	=8	8%	0.8	0.8%	——

SECOND TEST

In each of the following, select the answer which is the best value for the computation indicated at the left. Do not perform the computation, but select the best answer by inspection. You may assume that one of the four given answers is correct. Write the number of the correct answer on the line at the right as in Question 1.

		1	2	3	4	
1.	$(0.05)(3.76)$	=18.8	1.88	0.188	0.0188	3
2.	$0.006 \div 30$	=0.02	0.002	0.0002	0.00002	——
3.	$(7.22)(4.03)$	=2.91	29.1	291	2910	——
4.	$0.765 \div 0.03$	=255	25.5	2.55	0.255	——
5.	$\dfrac{(.03)(.12)}{40}$	=0.09	0.009	0.0009	0.00009	——
6.	$(0.08)^2$	=0.64	0.064	0.0064	0.00064	——
7.	$(0.2)^2$	=4.0	0.4	0.04	0.004	——
8.	$\sqrt{640}$	=8	80	25.3	2.53	——
9.	$\sqrt{0.0081}$	=0.9	0.09	0.28	0.028	——
10.	$\sqrt{1-(.4)^2}$	=0.92	0.84	0.60	0.96	——
11.	$\sqrt{2.5}$	=1.58	0.50	5	15.8	——
12.	$\sqrt{0.0625}$	=0.79	0.079	0.25	0.025	——
13.	$\sqrt{0.000009}$	=0.03	0.003	0.094	0.0094	——

		1	2	3	4	
14.	0.04	= .4	.400	.004	.040	——
15.	1.4	= .14%	.014%	1.4%	140%	——
16.	0.006	= 0.6%	6%	0.06%	0.006%	——
17.	(.2000)(15)	= 3	300.0	.0030	.3000	——

VI

SHORT CUTS IN COMPUTATION

Importance. This chapter is not intended for the person who expects to be a professional computer, but for the person who is inept in numerical work and who finds inaccuracy and slowness of computation a serious handicap in his study of elementary statistical methods. This discussion is planned for the person who expects to do a relatively small amount of computing, so that learning expert methods is not a wise investment of his time. The professional computer will use a computing machine and will master all the various checks and short cuts appropriate to its use, none of which are mentioned here. There is a steadily increasing literature relative to such devices, to which the professional computer is referred. Such a person will endeavor to reduce everything to mechanical processes, doing as little mental work as possible. There is, however, a large number of students whose main purpose in studying statistical method is not to learn to make extensive statistical studies but to understand and to interpret such. Since students of this type find themselves faced with the necessity of performing certain computations in order to develop statistical concepts, their main interest in studying computational methods is to effect an immediate economy of time. For such persons this section is written.

General Considerations. A prime essential for competent numerical work is an undivided mind. There is nothing more certain to produce errors in computation than allowing the attention to wander momentarily during the course of the work. A not uncommon cause of such inattention is fear. A student begins to add a column of figures. Halfway up the column he is distracted by the thought, "I make a great many mistakes in work of this sort. This time, however, I shall try very hard to be careful. Perhaps I have already made a mistake! I wonder if I ought to go back and start this column again?" By this time the damage has been done. Working very slowly and cautiously seems only to increase the tendency to errors due to momentary lapses of attention. Most persons do more accurate work when they achieve a certain abandon. At first it may seem sheer recklessness to compute at top speed, but eventually most persons develop thereby a concentration which tends to eliminate errors caused by fleeting daydreams.

Any person of even dull-normal intelligence can learn to perform the computations called for in statistical work, *if he really desires to do so.* Not infrequently, however, an adult has carried over from his grade-school arithmetic experiences a firm but unfounded belief in his own inability to deal with numbers, so that old fears and inhibitions make it difficult for him to give undivided attention to the problem at hand. A small amount of definite, determined practice often serves to eradicate the obstacles.

ADDITION

Combining Groups of Numbers. Speed and economy in adding comes largely from the ability to see at a glance the sum of a group of numbers, to think of numbers in groups. A person adding the figures in Example 1 will work slowly if he thinks "3, 9, 10, 12, 15, 20, 28, 35", and will save a good deal of time if he thinks of 3, 6, and 1 in a group, recognizing their sum instantly as 10, so that he can think, "10, 20, 35", adding by groups without attention to the individual numbers.

Example 1

$$
\begin{array}{r}
\left.\begin{array}{r}3\\6\\1\end{array}\right\}10\\[4pt]
\left.\begin{array}{r}2\\3\\5\end{array}\right\}10\\[4pt]
\left.\begin{array}{r}8\\7\end{array}\right\}15\\[2pt]
\hline
35
\end{array}
$$

EXERCISE 7

Practice adding the following columns in this fashion, then set down columns for yourself at random to afford as much further practice as you need. Add first by combining the numbers into groups of two as you go along the column, then later take larger groups into combination.

(a) 6	(b) 8	(c) 2	(d) 3	(e) 5	(f) 8	(g) 3	(h) 9
9	5	7	5	6	5	4	3
2	2	6	4	8	7	5	6
3	5	3	4	3	6	2	6
8	3	4	6	9	9	8	8
2	1	5	2	2	4	9	4
3	9	1	1	4	6	6	5
2	4	8	7	7	7	1	7
5	6	4	9	6	5	8	4
8	2	7	5	3	4	6	5
2	5	8	4	2	4	3	3

Adding Two Columns at Once. It is often convenient to add two columns at once, adding the ten's digit and the unit's digit separately. Thus in Example 2, we might think, adding downward, "35, 75, 82, 90, 150, 230, 237", or adding upward, "87, 95, 155, 195, 202, 207, 237". After a little practice one learns to take advantage of easy combinations for adding both digits at once. In Example 3 we might add downward "78, 80, **90**, 155, 165, 167, 170, **180**, 220, **223**", but it would require only a little practice to be able to omit all except the numbers printed in bold faced type. It is helpful to learn to recognize easy combinations which make multiples of ten, such as $65 + 12 + 13 = 90$.

Example 2

35
47
68
87
———
237

Example 3

78
12
65
12
13
43
———
223

Practice finding these sums, adding two columns at once, adding both upward and downward as a check.

(a) 63	(b) 27	(c) 87	(d) 91	(e) 63	(f) 75	(g) 68	(h) 15
25	13	91	87	86	96	16	24
92	59	76	62	95	91	97	29
67	62	32	17	21	82	25	73
35	87	19	47	16	44	86	38
41	45	28	36	24	27	83	35
15	43	53	39	72	94	72	49
82	28	46	24	84	33	16	63
43	36	17	33	21	87	23	13
52	24	29	72	76	22	46	29
15	92	44	41	84	93	72	47
25	16	45	54	19	46	84	53

Checking. Many mistakes in addition are made in carrying. To avoid these and to provide a check, it is helpful to set down the sum of each column separately when adding numbers of several digits, as in Example 4. As a check the columns may be added in reverse order, beginning with the left hand column, adding upward if the first addition was performed downward, and vice versa. See Check 1. Another check would be provided by adding two columns at a time, as in Check 2. In the example shown here an error has been purposely made in setting down the sum of the ten's column, to illustrate how the check would reveal such an error.

Example 4

```
3692
4875
2398
1647
4286
  28
  73
  25
  14
17258
```

Check 1

```
14
25
37
28
16898
```

Check 2

```
398
165
16898
```

Another method of checking is to divide the example into two parts, and to find the sum of each part separately, as in Example 5.

Set down numbers at random, add and check, until you feel confidence in your own accuracy.

Example 5

52463	
23897	
68456	
23874	168690
92901	
50325	
41006	
26583	
48761	259576
36	428266
43	
48	
33	
39	
428266	

MULTIPLICATION

Most of the short cuts which promote rapid multiplication are of relatively little value in statistical work. In general these short cuts are effected by performing a large part of the work mentally. The amateur computer would not receive sufficient return on his investment of time to make it profitable for him to learn to set down the product of 43×87 at sight. He can perform hundreds of such multiplications in the time it would take him to develop accuracy in the mental process. The professional computer has even less use for such mental short cuts, because his best means of improving the quality of his work is to make it more mechanical, not more mental. The more he attempts to carry in his mind, the more opportunities there are for error in his results. There are, however, a few short cuts which are of general usefulness.

Multiplication by Powers of Ten. Multiplying a number by 0.01, 0.1, 10, 100, 1000, or any other power of 10 is accomplished by setting the decimal point the appropriate number of places to the right or the left.

Multiplication by 25, 50, 75, 125. Since $25 = \frac{100}{4}$, the quickest way to multiply a number by 25 is to divide it by 4 and set the decimal point two places to the right. By doing this you divide by 4 and multiply by 100, which is equivalent to multiplying by 25. The product of $1473 \times 25 = \frac{147300}{4}$ $= 36825$. Since $0.5 = \frac{1}{2}$, $50 = \frac{100}{2}$, $5000 = \frac{10000}{2}$, the quickest way to multiply by such a number is to divide by 2 and move the decimal point to take care of the multiplication by the power of 10. Since $75 = \frac{300}{4}$, an easy way to multiply by 75 is to multiply by 3, divide by 4, and adjust the decimal point. To multiply by 125, divide by 8 and move the decimal point 3 places to the right. Multiplication by such numbers as 7.5, 12.5, 0.025, or 0.0125 may be similarly performed.

Exercise 9

Perform the following multiplications:

(1) 7.5×367

(2) 983.4×0.25

(3) 14.633×500

(4) 236×750

(5) 6837×1.25

(6) 86.3×2.5

(7) 1532×0.075

(8) 694×25

Multiplication by Numbers such as 299 or 396. When the multiplier is a little less than some integral multiple of 100, it is easy to multiply by the larger number and correct the result by subtraction. This general principle is also used in machine computation. The multiplication in Example 6 is based on the fact that $299 = 300 - 1$ and that therefore to multiply by 299 we can multiply by 300 and subtract the multiplicand. In Example 7 we have $396 = 400 - 4$, so that $723 \times 396 = 723 \times 400 - 723 \times 4$. In Example 8 we have $2997 = 3000 - 3$.

Example 6

$467 \times 299 = 139633$

$\underline{3}$

140100

$\underline{467}$

139633

Example 7

$723 \times 396 = 286308$

$\underline{4}$

2892

$\underline{2892}$

286308

Example 8

$49.31 \times 2.997 = 147.78207$

$\underline{3}$

14793

$\underline{14793}$

147.78207

EXERCISE 10

Perform the following multiplications, taking advantage of the device described in the preceding paragraph.

198×815	99×724	3996×1471
998×364	2.999×31.4	5998×862
1998×736	79.2×6.35	59.9×3.29

Squaring a Number Ending in 5. To square a two-place number ending in 5, multiply the ten's digit by one more than that digit and annex 25. Thus to square 85, multiply 8×9 and annex 25, the result being 7225. The explanation of this rule depends upon the formula for squaring a binomial as found in Chapter XV. Study the following illustrations.

$$(a+b)^2 = \quad a^2 + \ 2ab \quad\quad + b^2$$
$$(35)^2 = (30+5)^2 = \quad 30^2 + \ 2(30)(5) + 5^2$$
$$= \quad 30^2 + \ 10(30) + 5^2 = \quad (40)(30) + 5^2$$

$$(65)^2 = (60+5)^2 = 60^2 + 2(60)(5)+5^2$$
$$= 60^2 + 10(60)+5^2 = (70)(60)+5^2$$
$$(125)^2 = (120+5)^2 = 120^2+2(120)(5)+5^2$$
$$= 120^2+10(120)+5^2 = (130)(120)+5^2$$

Complete the following table by inspection:

$15^2 = \ 2\ 25$	$65^2 = 42\ 25$	$115^2 = 132\ 25$
$25^2 = \ 6\ 25$	$75^2 =$	$125^2 = 156\ 25$
$35^2 = 12\ 25$	$85^2 =$	$135^2 =$
$45^2 = 20\ 25$	$95^2 =$	$145^2 =$
$55^2 = 30\ 25$	$105^2 =$	$155^2 =$

Multiplication of Two Consecutive Numbers. If one knows the squares of all the numbers up to 20, it is easy to perform such a multiplication as 13×14 by thinking $13^2+13 = 182$. Thus

$$12 \times 13 = 12^2+12 = 156$$
$$13 \times 14 = 13^2+13 = 182$$
$$14 \times 15 = 14^2+14 = 210$$
$$15 \times 16 = 15^2+15 = 240$$

Any person who expects to do much statistical work will find it a convenience to know the squares of the numbers up to 20 or 25.

Checking. The best check for multiplication is to repeat the process, interchanging multiplier and multiplicand. The check by "casting out nines" cannot be recommended for statistical work. It is not infallible, and in particular it fails to detect the very common error of exchanging digits. Writing 28 instead of 82, or 364 instead of 463 is a type of mistake which even fairly good computers make occasionally. "Casting out nines" does not reveal errors of this type.

A slide rule provides an admirable check for multiplication, division and square root. The slide rule is far less useful than a computing machine for most statistical work, but to the person working without a machine it is a valuable aid, especially as a check on other computation.[1]

DIVISION

Short cuts in division are based chiefly on the fact that multiplication is easier and quicker than division and that short division is easier and quicker than long division. The more digits there are in the divisor, the more desirable it is to utilize a short cut.

Division by Factors. To divide by 24 we can divide successively by 4 and 6, or by 8 and 3, thus substituting two easy short divisions for one long division. Compare the number of figures in Examples 9 and 10.

Example 9

$$24)\overline{32265} 5)\overline{1344.375}$$
$$\underline{24}$$
$$82$$
$$\underline{72}$$
$$106$$
$$\underline{96}$$
$$105$$
$$\underline{96}$$
$$90$$
$$\underline{72}$$
$$180$$
$$\underline{168}$$
$$120$$
$$\underline{120}$$

Example 10

$$4)\overline{32265}$$
$$6)\overline{8066.25}$$
$$1344.375$$

$$8)\overline{32265}$$
$$3)\overline{4033.125}$$
$$1344.375$$

Multiplication by factors does not in general afford a great saving of time, although it provides a possible check on other multiplication.

---

[1] Keuffel and Esser publish a very complete manual of instructions for the use of the slide rule.

Perform the following divisions, utilizing the device of successive divisions by factors, and check. Perform one or two of the computations by long division in order to compare the amount of time required for the two methods.

$946.5 \div 18$	$17.683 \div 5.6$	$369.21 \div 6300$
$1.037 \div 32$	$253.41 \div 0.54$	$5281.3 \div 35$
$72.35 \div 3.6$	$913.46 \div 0.48$	$792.57 \div 6.4$
$324.9 \div 27$	$25.623 \div 210$	$2.1478 \div 4.5$
$8289 \div 420$	$5.6134 \div 72$	$47.263 \div 1.6$

Division by Equivalent Multiplication. Time can often be saved in division by recognition of the principle that division by a number is equivalent to multiplication by the reciprocal of the number. The reciprocal of a number is the result of dividing 1 by that number. Thus $\frac{1}{4}$, 5, $\frac{2}{3}$, and .02064 are respectively the reciprocals of 4, $\frac{1}{5}$, $\frac{3}{2}$, and 48.45. (See Chapter X on Fractions.) Thus $a \div \dfrac{b}{c} = a \times \dfrac{c}{b}$. Study the following illustrations.

Equivalence	Rule	Application
$25 = \dfrac{100}{4}$	To divide by 25, multiply by 4 and set decimal point two places to the left	$317 \div 25 = 12.68$ $\underline{4}$ 1268
$50 = \dfrac{100}{2}$	To divide by 50, multiply by 2 and move decimal point two places to the left	$678 \div 50 = 13.56$ $\underline{2}$ 1356
$75 = \dfrac{300}{4}$	To divide by 75, multiply by 4, divide by 3, and set decimal point two places to the left	$686 \div 75 = 9.1467$ $\underline{4}$ $3\overline{)2744}$ 914.67
$375 = \dfrac{3000}{8}$	To divide by 375, multiply by 8, divide by 3, and set decimal point three places to the left	$1486 \div 375 = 3.96267$ $\underline{8}$ $3\overline{)11888}$ 3962.67

Equivalence	Rule	Application
$15 = \dfrac{30}{2}$	To divide by 15, multiply by 2, divide by 3, and set decimal point one place to the left	$3372 \div 15 = 224.8$ $\dfrac{2}{}$ $3)\overline{6744}$ $\overline{2248}$

Study the placing of the decimal point in the following:

$$0.317 \div 0.25 = 1.268 \qquad 1486 \div 3.75 = 396.267$$
$$317 \div 2.5 = 126.8 \qquad 678 \div 5000 = 0.1356$$
$$3170 \div 250 = 12.68 \qquad 678 \div 0.5 = 1356$$
$$6860 \div 7.5 = 914.67 \qquad 3372 \div 1.5 = 2248$$
$$686 \div 0.75 = 914.67 \qquad 3372 \div 0.15 = 22480$$

Exercise 12

Perform the following divisions and check results. (See below for methods of checking.)

$$372 \div 75 \qquad 9.241 \div 25 \qquad 5621 \div 150$$
$$1468 \div 500 \qquad 86.48 \div 3.75 \qquad 237 \div 7.5$$
$$13.24 \div 1.5 \qquad 6297 \div 45 \qquad 0.682 \div 0.05$$

Table of Reciprocals. Division by a number n is obviously equivalent to multiplication by $\dfrac{1}{n}$. Published tables of reciprocals are available (e.g., Barlow's *Tables of Squares, Cubes, Square Roots, Cube Roots and Reciprocals*, London, E. & F. N. Spon, Ltd.) from which one may read the value of $\dfrac{1}{n}$ for any number up to 100000. One of the easiest ways to divide by a large number is to look up its reciprocal in such a table and to multiply that reciprocal by the dividend. This method is much used in machine computation.

Checking. The best check for division is multiplication. When there is no remainder, the product of the quotient and the divisor should exactly equal the dividend. When there is

a remainder, if it is added to the product of the quotient and
the divisor, the result should be equal to the dividend.

Division by successive factors may be checked by reversing
the order of the factors. This of course does not guard against
a mistake in selecting the factors.

One of the best checks for any sort of computation is the
habit of estimating the answer in advance. (See pages 35
and 36.) This is a valuable safeguard in work with decimals.

VII

ALGEBRAIC SYMBOLISM

INITIAL TEST

After taking this test, compare your answers with the key in the back of the book. If you have made any errors, study the explanations and practice exercises and take the second test.

1. If x_1, x_2, x_3, and x_4 are four numbers, what will represent
   (1) The product of the first and third divided by the sum of the second and fourth?
   (2) The result of multiplying the first by the sum of the other three?
   (3) The sum of the first two subtracted from the sum of the last two?

2. Translate the following rules into formulas. The letters in parentheses are suggested as appropriate to use, and are the ones used in making up the answer key.

   (1) The present value (P) of a sum of money (S) due at some future time (t) may be found by dividing that sum by 1 plus the product of the rate (r) and the time (t).
   (2) The distance in feet (d) passed over by a freely falling body is approximately equal to 16 times the square of the time in seconds (t) during which it falls.
   (3) In a particular city, taxi-cab fares (F) are 25¢ for the first $\frac{1}{4}$ mile, 15¢ for each additional $\frac{1}{4}$ mile, and 5¢ for each 3 minutes of waiting time. (F = number of cents in fare, m = number of quarter miles traveled, w = number of minutes waiting time.)
   (4) The volume of a sphere (V) is equal to one-sixth of π times the cube of the diameter (d).

(5) If the difference of two numbers is subtracted from the sum of the same numbers, the result is always twice the number which was subtracted in finding the first difference. (n, n')

3. The total score (S) on a test is made up from the scores on three parts. The first part (P') is given a weight of 2, the second (P'') of 3, and the third (P''') of 1. What is the total score?

4. A class is given one form of a test in November (F) and a second form of the same test in March (F'). Using subscripts to designate children, write a formula for the gain made by the first child.

5. In a true false test of n statements, the score is obtained by subtracting the number wrong from the number right.

(1) If all the questions are marked, and w are wrong, how many are right? (R, n, w)

(2) If all the questions are marked, and w are wrong, what is the score? (S, n, w)

(3) If q questions are omitted, and w are wrong, how many are right? (R, n, q, w)

(4) If q questions are omitted, and w are wrong, what is the score? (S, n, q, w)

Practical Importance. The language of statistical method is highly symbolic, and to achieve any real understanding of statistics it is essential to be able to *think* in terms of symbols. The student who is not trained in mathematical methods and who has been accustomed to think only in verbal patterns usually experiences difficulty in reading texts on statistics until he acquires some degree of fluency in using the language of symbolism. One reason why many people find statistical method difficult is that for them a formula has never taken life, has never become a dynamic and concise statement of a general principle or relation, but remains static, artificial, arbitrary, unintelligible. It is not even enough that the student should acquire the ability to translate from symbolism into words; he should be able to use symbolism as a language in which to express his own ideas. This ability is not difficult to acquire.

This section presents the more elementary aspects of formula making in general, and should be mastered in order to understand Chapter XIII in which the material deals with symbolism used particularly in statistical method.

Symbolism. In using algebraic symbolism, the following should be kept in mind.

1. The first letter of a word is often used to represent a number. The number of males in a statistical study might be represented by m and the number of females by f, the number of adults by a, and the number of children by c. This would sometimes be impractical, as, for example, in a study of differences between city school children and country school children, and therefore the letters x, y, and z, are commonly used instead of the more suggestive initial letters of words. Whether the letters used in an algebraic expression suggest words or not, *they always represent numbers*.

2. Subscripts are used like adjectives. Thus to distinguish the number of boys in a school system from the number of girls we might write N_B and N_G, or n_B, n_G, or N_1, N_2, or n_1, n_2, but we would *not* write NB and NG. The latter is not only poor form but is likely to result in misunderstanding. See **6** below. The mean salary paid to teachers in cities A, B, and C might be indicated as M_A, M_B, M_C, or S_A, S_B, S_C, or M_1, M_2, M_3, or S_1, S_2, S_3, but *not* MA, MB, MC, and *not* MSA, MSB, MSC. If one wanted to write about the mean salary paid teachers in cities A, B, and C and also about the mean number of pupils taught by the teachers in these schools, a double system of subscripts might be used, as M_{SA}, M_{SB}, M_{SC}, and M_{PA}, M_{PB}, M_{PC}, or $_AM_S$, $_BM_S$, $_CM_S$, and $_AM_P$, $_BM_P$, $_CM_P$, but *not* MSA and MPA. *A number should be represented by a single letter*, not by two or more written on the same line.

3. Primes and double primes may be used in much the same way as subscripts. Thus three numbers might be indicated by n, n', and n''. The score of one child on an initial test might be T_1, and the score of the same child on a second test might be T_1'. For a second child we could have T_2 and T_2', for a third child T_3 and T_3', etc. It is often useful to combine primes and subscripts in this fashion, rather than to use a subscript of a subscript as was done in the previous paragraph.

4. To increase the number of available forms, both capitals and small letters are used by scientific workers, and often the Greek alphabet is employed also. Thus we might designate scores on three forms of an arithmetic test as A, a, α, or A, A', A'', or A_1, A_2, A_3.

5. Signs like ft., bu., in., $, yr., lb., etc., are not used in algebraic formulas, because the formula is a statement of relation between pure numbers.

6. The multiplication sign $\times$ is not often used in algebraic formulas. The product of two numbers, represented say by a and b, would usually be expressed by writing the letters together with no sign between them, as ab. Sometimes a dot raised above the base line is written between the two numbers which are to be multiplied, as $a \cdot b$, but the form ab is much more common. Thus to indicate the product of the number of teachers employed in city A by the number of dollars in the mean salary paid in that city we might write $N_A M_A$ or $N_A S_A$ or $n_A s_A$, or many other similar expressions.

7. The sign $\div$ is almost never used in algebraic formulas. The quotient of a divided by b is usually written $\dfrac{a}{b}$ or a/b but not often $a \div b$.

8. Parentheses or brackets, ( ), { }, or [ ], may be used to show that an expression of more than one term is to be treated as one number. Sometimes parentheses are placed around numbers which are to be multiplied together when there seems to be danger of confusion otherwise, as $(6.2)(5.1)$.

9. When a number is used more than once as a factor, this is indicated by an exponent. Thus $7 \times 7 \times 7 \times 7 = 7^4$, $15 \times 15 \times 15 \times 15 \times 15 \times 15 = 15^6$, and $r \cdot r \cdot r = r^3$. Notice that an exponent has mathematical meaning, whereas a subscript is merely descriptive.

10. In writing one times a number the 1 is omitted. Thus $\frac{1}{3}$ of $6n$ is $2n$ but $\frac{1}{3}$ of $3n$ is written n, not $1n$, and $7x - 6x = x$, not $1x$.

Exercise 13

1. If n represents a given number, what will represent

    (1) Twice that number
    (2) Three more than the number
    (3) Seven less than 5 times the number
    (4) The product of the number and itself
    (5) Six divided by the number
    (6) The result of dividing 20 by two more than the number
    (7) The result of multiplying 5 more than the number by 2 less the number
    (8) The square of twice the number
    (9) Twice the square of the number

2. If n_1, n_2, n_3, and n_4 are four numbers, what will represent
    (1) The sum of the four numbers
    (2) The product of the four numbers
    (3) The sum of the first two numbers multiplied by the sum of the last two
    (4) The result of subtracting the sum of the four numbers from the product of the four
    (5) The result of dividing the sum of the first two numbers by the sum of the last two
    (6) The first number multiplied by the sum of the other three

(7) The quotient obtained by dividing the third number by the sum of the others

(8) The result of multiplying 10 times the first number by 4 times the second and dividing this product by 6 times the third number

3. Study the correspondence between words and symbols in the following:

Verbal Expression	*Symbolic Expression*
Think of any number	x
Add 15	$x+15$
Multiply the result by 2	$2(x+15)=2x+30$
Subtract the original number	$2x+30-x=x+30$
Add 5	$x+30+5=x+35$
Subtract the original number	$x+35-x=35$

No matter what number was chosen in the beginning, the remainder is now 35.

4. Write the symbolic equivalent for each step in the following:

Think of any number
Double it
Add 40
Multiply the result by 3
Subtract 100
Subtract twice the original number
Divide by 4
The result is now 5 more than the number chosen in the beginning.

5. Write the symbolic equivalent for each step in the following:

Think of any number
Add 25
Multiply this sum by 4
Add the original number
Divide by 5
Multiply the result by 2
Subtract 40
The remainder is twice the original number.

6. Below are sentences which are to be translated into the shorthand of algebra. The letters inclosed in parentheses after each sentence are the letters which have been used in the key. Any other letters which seem appropriate could of course be used just as well. For example, the sentence "There are two numbers such that if 5 times the first is subtracted from twice the second the result will be 12" might be translated as $2x-5y=12$, $2y-5x=12$, $2n_2-5n_1=12$, $2x_2-5x_1=12$, or in a vast number of other correct ways.

(1) There are two numbers whose sum is 45. (n_1, n_2)

(2) There are two numbers whose difference is 6. (x_1, x_2)

(3) There are two numbers such that $\frac{1}{2}$ of the first plus $\frac{1}{3}$ of the second is 20. (x, y)

(4) If three times a number is added to 7 times the same number, the result will be 10 times the number. (n)

(5) There are three numbers whose sum is 90. (n_1, n_2, n_3)

(6) In a particular class, there are 5 more girls than boys. (N_G, N_B)

(7) The number of pupils in all the schools of a particular city is made up of the number of pupils in the high schools plus the number in the grades plus the number in the kindergartens. (N_C, N_H, N_G, N_K)

(8) If 7 times any number is subtracted from 8 times that number, the remainder will be the number. (x)

7. Write a formula for

(1) The total surface of a rectangular solid. (S, l, w, h)

(2) The volume of a rectangular solid. (V, l, w, h)

(3) The interest on a given principal, for a given time at a given rate. (i, P, r, t)

(4) The value in cents (V_C) of a pile of coins in which there are d dimes, n nickels, q quarters, and p pennies.

(5) A taxi fare if the rate is 15¢ for the first quarter mile and 10¢ for each additional quarter mile plus 5¢ for each 3 minutes of waiting time. (F=fare in cents, q=number of quarter miles traveled, w=number of minutes of waiting time[1]

(6) The reading on a Centigrade thermometer when the reading on a Fahrenheit scale is known. (C, F)

(7) The reading on a Fahrenheit scale when the reading on a Centigrade scale is known (F, C).

8. Translate the following into words:

(1) $n_1 + n_2 = 17$

(2) $n_1 = 2n_2$

(3) $4x + 3y = 50$

(4) $\dfrac{n_1 + n_2}{n_3} = 5$

(5) $x = y + 7$

(6) $2x + 3 = y$

(7) $6n + 5n = 11n$

(8) $50x - 20x = 30x$

SECOND TEST

1. If n_1, n_2, and n_3 are three numbers, what will represent

(1) The sum of the first two divided by the third

(2) The result of multiplying the second number by the sum of the other two

(3) The product of all three numbers

2. Translate the following rules into formulas. The letters in parentheses are suggested as appropriate to use, and are the ones used in making up the answer key.

(1) The area of a trapezoid is equal to one-half the altitude times the sum of the two bases. (A, h, b_1, b_2)

(2) If a sum of money is put at interest for a given period, the amount at the end of that time will be equal to the principal multiplied by 1 plus the product of the rate and the time. (A, P, r, t)

(3) The area of the surface of a sphere is 4 times π times the square of the radius. (A, r)

(4) To send a parcel post package to a given place costs 8 cents for the first pound and 6 cents for each additional pound. (Let $C =$ cost in cents, $w =$ weight of package in pounds.)

(5) The result of adding 3 times the sum of two numbers and 5 times the sum of these numbers is always 8 times the sum of the numbers. (n, n')

3. The total score on a test is made up from the scores on three parts. In the composite, the first part is given a weight of 1, the second part of 3, and the third part of 4. What is the total score? (S_{T}, s_1, s_2, s_3)

4. A class took an initial test in October and a final test on the same subject in December (T and T'). Using subscripts to designate children, write a formula for the gain made by child 5.

5. In a true false test of t questions, the score was obtained by subtracting the number wrong from the number right.

(1) If all the questions were answered, and r of them were right, how many were wrong? (w, t, r)

(2) If all the questions were answered and r of them were right, what was the score? (S, t, r)

(3) If n were omitted and r were right, how many were wrong? (w, t, r, n)

(4) If n were omitted, and r were right, what was the score? (S, t, r, n)

VIII

SIGNED NUMBERS

INITIAL TEST

After taking this test, compare your answers with the key in the back of the book. If you have made any errors, study the explanations and practice exercises and take the second test.

1. Find the results of carrying out the indicated operations.

(1) $(2a-b+3c)-2(5c-a+x-2)$

(2) $(2x-3y-1)+3(y-2x-3)$

(3) $-4(a-2n+4)$

(4) $(6p-12q+18r-6)\div(-3)$

2. Place a check mark in front of each of the following which is *necessarily* a positive number no matter whether the letters themselves have positive or negative values.

(1) a	(7) $\sqrt{4a^2}$	(13) $ab+ac+bc$
(2) $a+b+c$	(8) $(a^2)^3$	(14) abc
(3) a^2	(9) $(-a)^2$	(15) $(\frac{1}{3}a^2+b^2+c^2)$
(4) a^3	(10) $(-a)^3$	(16) $\sqrt{a^2b^2c^2}$
(5) $a^3+b^3+c^3$	(11) $(-a)^4$	(17) $\sqrt[3]{a}$
(6) $a^2+b^2+c^2$	(12) ab	(18) $\sqrt[3]{a^2}$

3. In the following expressions, suppose that none of the variables has the value zero, although any or all of them may be negative. It follows that some of the expressions may be negative in value or may be zero when positive and negative values exactly balance, while others can be only positive. Place a check mark in front of each expression for which zero is a possible value.

(1) $x+y+z+w$	(4) $x^4+y^4+z^4+w^4$
(2) $x^2+y^2+z^2+w^2$	(5) $\sqrt{x}+\sqrt{y}+\sqrt{z}+\sqrt{w}$
(3) $x^3+y^3+z^3+w^3$	(6) $\sqrt[3]{x}+\sqrt[3]{y}+\sqrt[3]{z}+\sqrt[3]{w}$

Meaning of Negative Sign. When we wish to distinguish between opposite directions from a common starting point, we usually consider one direction as positive and the other negative. Thus if a man travels 10 miles east from A, we may record his distance from A as $+10$, while if another man travels 10 miles west from A, we may record his distance from A as -10. Their journeys are equally long but in opposite directions. In the same way 16° above zero is commonly written $+16°$, and 16° below zero written $-16°$.

-4	-3	-2	-1	A	1	2	3	4	5

Thus a minus sign has two meanings. It may be used as a symbol of operation to indicate that subtraction is to be performed. It may also be used to indicate direction from an origin. In practice this double use causes no confusion whatever.

Absolute Value of a Number. The plus sign as a symbol of direction is commonly omitted, and when we see a number with no sign before it we understand it to be positive. Thus 60 is understood to mean $+60$, and 0.5 is understood to mean $+0.5$. Sometimes we wish to direct our attention to the size of a number without regard to its sign. Thus we may speak of a journey of 5 miles, telling the extent of the journey without stating its direction, or we may speak of a change of 10° in temperature without telling whether the change is up or down. The size of a number irrespective of its direction is called its *absolute value*, or its *numerical value*, or sometimes its *arithmetic value*. If n is any number, positive or negative, the absolute value of n is written $|n|$. Algebraically $+1$ is larger than -1, but numerically they are equal. Algebraically -3 is smaller than -2, but numerically the first is larger. The absolute value of 5 is smaller than the absolute value of -8, but on a scale of directed values, 5 would be the larger.

Addition and Subtraction of Signed Numbers.

Rule 1. (a) To add numbers with the same sign, add the absolute values of the numbers and prefix the common sign.

(b) To add two numbers with unlike signs, find the difference in their absolute values and prefix the sign of the larger number.

(c) To add several numbers with unlike signs, add the positive numbers and the negative numbers separately by rule (a), then add the two sums by rule (b).

Rule 2. To subtract one signed number from another, consider the sign of the subtrahend to be changed and proceed as in algebraic addition.

Exercise 14

1. Arrange the following numbers in order of their algebraic values, beginning with the smallest:

$$2, \ -3.6, \ -5, \ 0, \ -0.1, \ 4.3, \ 0.5, \ -0.7$$

2. Arrange the same numbers in order of their absolute values, beginning with the smallest.

3. Add:

$$
\begin{array}{lll}
(1) \quad -43 & (3) \quad +12 & (5) \quad 13 \\
 \quad \underline{-\ 7} & \quad \underline{-\ 5} & \quad \underline{-1} \\
\\
(2) \quad -20 & (4) \quad 0 & (6) \quad -5 \\
 \quad \underline{+\ 6} & \quad \underline{+16} & \quad \underline{0} \\
\end{array}
$$

4. In Exercise **3** above, subtract the lower number from the upper.

5. Add:

(1)
$$
\begin{array}{r}
3x-2y+\ 5 \\
-\ x+\ y-\ 7 \\
-4x-5y+10 \\
\underline{x+6y-\ 2} \\
\end{array}
$$

(2)
$$
\begin{array}{r}
p-4q+\ r \\
\underline{q-3r+s} \\
\end{array}
$$

(3)
$$
\begin{array}{r}
n-4r-s \\
\underline{2n-\ r-s} \\
\end{array}
$$

6. Subtract the second number from the first:

(1) $c - 4d + f$
   $\underline{c - 5d - 3f}$

(2) $5x + 2y - 3w$
   $\underline{-x + 4y - 3w}$

(3) $2k - 3t + 4m - 2$
   $\underline{t - 3m - 6 + n}$

Multiplication of Signed Numbers. Every one is familiar with the fact that multiplication by an integer is merely a short method of performing repeated addition, and that therefore our rules for multiplication are merely rules for finding the results of repeated addition. Thus $3(6) = 6 + 6 + 6$ and $5a = a + a + a + a + a$. Perform the four additions, and then summarize your results by writing the values of the products indicated below.

-1	$2a$	$-3ab$	$x - 5y + 2w$	$-a + 10b - 4$
-1	$2a$	$-3ab$	$x - 5y + 2w$	$\underline{-a + 10b - 4}$
-1	$2a$	$-3ab$	$\underline{x - 5y + 2w}$	
-1	$2a$	$\underline{-3ab}$		
$\underline{-1}$	$2a$			
	$\underline{2a}$			

$5(-1) = ?$ $4(-3ab) = ?$ $2(-a + 10b - 4) = ?$

$6(2a) = ?$ $3(x - 5y + 2w) = ?$

In the section dealing with the order of operations, we saw that changing the order of factors would not affect their product. Therefore $5(-1) = (-1)(5) = -5$ and $4(-3ab) = (-3ab)(4) = -12ab$. It is safe to generalize, then, and say that the *product of a positive number and a negative number is a negative number.*

We must now consider the product of two negative numbers, and the rule for the sign of such a product may be discovered by a study of the following identities:

$6(8-12) = \quad 48-72 = -24$ which agrees with
$$6(8-12) = 6(-4) = -24.$$

$-3(2+5) = -6-15 = -21$ which agrees with
$$-3(2+5) = -3(7) = -21.$$

Now while we have not yet agreed as to the value of $(-4)(-3)$, still we can agree that $-4(7-3)$ must be equal to $-4(4)$ or -16. Therefore $(-4)(-3)$ must be a number which will make $-4(7-3)$ equal to -16. Now $-4(7-3) = -4(7)+(-4)(-3) = -28+(-4)(-3) = -16$, and therefore $(-4)(-3)$ must be a number which can be added to -28 so that the sum will be -16. This number is $+12$. Further study of such illustrations would lead us to

Rule 3.   (a) When two numbers have like signs their product is positive, when they have unlike signs their product is negative.

      (b) When a product contains an odd number of negative factors, it is negative; when it contains an even number of negative factors, or no negative factors, it is positive.

Division of Signed Numbers. By carefully working through the questions below, you should discover the rule for the sign of a quotient. It must be remembered that division is the reverse of multiplication, that if $ab = c$, then $a = c \div b$ and $b = c \div a$.

(1) $(-5)(-2) =$ ——— and therefore $10 \div (-5) =$ ———

(2) $(6)(5) \quad\;\; =$ ——— and therefore $30 \div 5 \quad\;\; =$ ———

(3) $(-1)(-1) =$ ——— and therefore $1 \div (-1) =$ ———

(4) $(5)(-3) \quad =$ ——— and therefore $-15 \div (-3) =$ ———

(5) $(20)(-3) =$ ——— and therefore $-60 \div 20 \quad =$ ———

(6) $(-1)(7) \quad =$ ——— and therefore $-7 \div (-1) =$ ———

A generalization suggested by these answers is:

Rule 4. When two numbers have like signs their quotient is positive and when they have unlike signs their quotient is negative.

Exponents. The repetition of a factor in a product is usually indicated by the use of an exponent. Thus

$$a \times a \times a = a^3, \qquad 2 \times 2 \times 2 \times 2 \times 2 = 2^5,$$
$$(xyz)(3xy)(4xz) = 12x^3y^2z^2,$$

It should be noted that $x = x^1$ and $n = n^1$. The first power of a number is usually written without any exponent.

Division of a Monomial by a Monomial. A *monomial* is an algebraic expression of one term, such as $13a$, $\dfrac{2b}{c}$, $\dfrac{5a^3n}{2x}$.

A *binomial* is an algebraic expression of two terms, such as $x + 3y$, $a^3 + b^3$, or $4npq - \dfrac{3p^2q^2}{n}$.

A *trinomial* is an algebraic expression of three terms, such as $a^2 + 2ab + b^2$ or $n^3 - 2n^2 + 1$. A *polynomial* is an algebraic expression of more than one term, such as $c + d$, $x^2 - 3x + 2$, $n^4 - 3n^2 + 2n - 5$, or $a^6 + 7a^5 - 2a^4 + a^3 - 3$.

Division of a monomial by a monomial involves little difficulty beyond attention to signs and exponents.

Divide $28a^2b^3c$ by $2ab^2c$.

We may write this $\dfrac{28a^2b^3c}{2ab^2c} = \dfrac{28aabbbc}{2abbc}$.

Since division of both terms of a fraction by the same number does not change the value of the fraction, therefore

$$\frac{28a^2b^3c}{2ab^2c} = 14ab$$

Perform the following divisions:

(1) $6a^5 \div 2a^3$

(2) $12x^3y^4 \div 3x^2y$

(3) $x^7 \div x^3$

(4) $15n^6 \div 3n^2$

In general, when m is larger than n, $x^m \div x^n = x^{m-n}$. The value of $x^m \div x^n$ when m is not larger than n will be considered later.

Multiplication of a Polynomial by a Monomial. We have already seen that $3(x-5y+2w) = 3x-15y+6w$. In general, to multiply a polynomial by a monomial, *every term* of the polynomial must be multiplied by the monomial. When the monomial multiplier is positive, the signs of the terms in the polynomial are not changed, when the multiplier is negative, the sign of every term in the polynomial is changed. In such an expression as $3(x-y)-(2x-y)$ we may consider that the expression $2x-y$ is multiplied by -1.

Division of a Polynomial by a Monomial. Again we will find the process of division by reversing the process of multiplication with which we are already familiar. Study the first two statements below until their meaning is clear, then complete the remaining statements by filling in the blanks.

(1) $3(2a+x-3y) = 6a+3x-9y$,

  therefore $(6a+3x-9y) \div 3 = 2a+x-3y$.

(2) $-a(a-3b+1) = -a^2+3ab-a$,

  therefore $(-a^2+3ab-a) \div (-a) = a-3b+1$.

(3) $-xy(x^2-y^2) = -x^3y+xy^3$,

  therefore $(-x^3y+xy^3) \div (-xy) =$ ——————.

(4) $7(x-y+4) = 7x-7y+28$,

  therefore $(7x-7y+28) \div 7 =$ ——————.

(5) $2b(a+3b-c) =$ ——————,

  therefore $(2ab+6b^2-2bc) \div 2b =$ ——————.

(6) $-n(n^2-3) =$ ——————,

  therefore $(-n^3+3n) \div (-n) =$ ——————.

(7) $-2r^2(s-3r+1) =$ ——————,

  therefore $(-2r^2s+6r^3-2r^2) \div (-2r^2) =$ ——————.

(8) $-(x-2y+5) =$ ——————,

  therefore $(-x+2y-5) \div (-1) =$ ——————.

When a polynomial is to be divided by a monomial, every separate term of the polynomial must be divided by the monomial.

Sign of a Power. By the rule for the sign of a product, we see that every odd power of a negative number is negative, and every even power is positive. Of course every power of a positive number is positive.

Sign of a Root. We know that $(+a)(+a) = +a^2$,
and that $\qquad (-a)(-a) = +a^2$.

Consequently a^2 has two square roots, $+a$ and $-a$. If, then, we know that $a^2 = 25$, we write $a = \pm 5$. However it is customary to use $\sqrt{25}$ to mean the positive root, or $+5$, and to write $-\sqrt{25}$ when we mean -5. Thus $\sqrt{a}$ is a positive number, just as any other number not preceded by a sign is considered to be positive. To indicate both roots of the number x we must use the double sign, writing $\pm\sqrt{x}$. This sign is read "plus or minus." It would be correct to write

$$x^2 = 49, \text{ therefore } x = \pm 7$$

It would not be correct to write

$$x = \sqrt{64}, \text{ therefore } x = \pm 8.$$

Since all odd powers have the same sign as their roots, then it must follow that an odd root has always the same sign as its power. Consequently $\sqrt[3]{a}$ or $\sqrt[5]{a}$ must be a positive number when a is positive and a negative number when a is negative, just as a^3, a^5, a^7, a^9, etc., are positive numbers when a is positive and negative numbers when a is negative. We will rule out of consideration the even roots of negative numbers. These involve what are known as "imaginary numbers" and are not needed for an understanding of elementary statistical methods.

We see then that a^2, a^4, a^6, and in general a^{2n} are positive numbers no matter whether a is positive or negative. There-

fore $a^2+b^2+c^2+d^2$ must be positive, as must
$$x_1^4+x_2^4+x_3^4+\cdots+x_n^4.$$
But a^3, a^5, a^7, etc., may be either positive or negative, and consequently $a^3+b^3+c^3$ might be positive, might be negative, or might be zero if positive and negative numbers exactly balance. Since a^2 is positive, $\sqrt[3]{a^2}$ and $(a^2)^3$ must both be positive.

Inverse Operations. Raising a number to the nth power and taking the nth root are inverse operations. There are in mathematics several such pairs of operations, so connected that the effect of one operation cancels the effect of the other. Familiar examples are addition and subtraction, multiplication and division. Study the following questions and answers to see their parallelism.

	Answer
What is the cost of an article which costs $5?	$5
What is the name of the man whose name is Scott?	Scott
What is the square root of a number whose square root is 6?	6
What is the square root of a number which is the square of n?	n
What is the square of a number whose square is x?	x
What is the square of the square root of r?	r

Symbolic statements similar to the foregoing are:

$$\sqrt{2^2} = 2$$
$$(\sqrt{r})^2 = r$$
$$\sqrt{(x-a)^2} = x-a$$
$$\left(\sqrt{\frac{pq}{n}}\right)^2 = \frac{pq}{n}$$
$$\left(\frac{\sigma}{\sqrt{n}}\right)^2 = \frac{\sigma^2}{n}$$
$$(\sqrt{1-r^2})^2 = 1-r^2$$

Translate each of these statements from symbols into words.

EXERCISE 15

1. Perform the indicated operations.

(1) $(-3)(-5)$

(2) $(-7)(6)$

(3) $(4)(-3)$

(4) $(-1)(-9)$

(5) $(0)(-6)$

(6) $(4.5)(-3.2)$

(7) $a(3a)$

(8) $\left(\dfrac{1}{x}\right)(2x)$

(9) $\sqrt[3]{-8}$

(10) $(-3)^2$

(11) $(-4)^1$

(12) $(-1)^3$

(13) $(-2)^4$

(14) $(+2)^3$

(15) $(-2)^3$

(16) $(-a)^2$

(17) $(a)^2$

(18) $(-a)^3$

(19) $\sqrt{16}$

(20) $\sqrt{64}$

(21) $\sqrt[3]{64}$

(22) $\sqrt[3]{-64}$

(23) $(-\tfrac{1}{2})^3$

(24) $=\sqrt{25}$

(25) $-\sqrt{81}$

(26) $=\sqrt{36}$

(27) $\sqrt{a^2}$

(28) $(\sqrt{a^2})^3$

(29) $(\sqrt{-a})^2$

(30) $(-12)\div(-2)$

(31) $(3a)(-5a)(-2a)$

(32) $(-4a)^2$

(33) $(-3x)^3$

(34) $(36a^2+5a)(-2a)$

(35) $(xy)(2x^2)(-3y)$

(36) $(-3n)(4n^2)$

(37) $\sqrt{(a+b)^2}$

(38) $\sqrt{(-3)^2}$

(39) $\sqrt{(-3n)^2}$

(40) $(\sqrt{pq})^2$

(41) $-3(a-2b)$

(42) $(-2a^2)(-3b^2)$

(43) $2xy(3x-4y)$

(44) $(3a-4b)-(a-2b+c)$

(45) $(2x+7y-1)-(x-y)-3$

(46) $3(r+2n)-2(n-4-3r)$

(47) $r(n-2)-3(n+r)$

(48) $ax-a(x+2y)+x(3a-y)$

(49) $a^2-2a(a-b+3c)-a(b-c)$

(50) $5+2(x-3)-4(y+3)$

(51) $ac+b(a+c)-c(a-b)$

(52) $(10p+12q-8)\div(-2)$

(53) $(x-15xy+18z)\div2x$

(54) $(6a-12ab+12ac)\div12a$

(55) $(4xy+2y-6y^2)\div(-2y)$

(56) $(16ax^2-12a^2+8ax)\div(-12a)$

(57) $(6-18x+24y)\div(-6)$

(58) $(pqr-2pqs)\div(-pq)$

(59) $(-19c+10a-3)\div(-1)$

(60) $(24a^2-36ab+18ac)\div(-3a)$

2. Find the value of each of the following expressions when the letters have the indicated values:

(1) $x^2+y^2+z^2$ when $x=-1$, $y=-2$, and $z=-3$

(2) $xy+xz+yz$ when $x=-1.6$, $y=2$, $z=8$

(3) $ab+ac+bc$ when $a=-1$, $b=-2$, $c=-3$

(4) $pq+pr+ps$ when $p=2$, $r=-3$, $s=-4$, $q=6$

(5) $\sqrt{pqr}$ when $p=12$, $q=1$, $r=3$

(6) $3a^2 \div 2a$ when $a=-6$

(7) $\dfrac{a-bc}{ef}$ when $a=43$, $b=-3$, $c=4$, $e=-2$, $f=5$

(8) $\dfrac{a-bc}{\sqrt{1-b^2}\,\sqrt{1-c^2}}$ when $a=-.16$, $b=-.60$, and $c=-.80$

(9) $\dfrac{a-bc}{\sqrt{1-b^2}\,\sqrt{1-c^2}}$ when $a=-.96$, $b=+.60$, and $c=+.80$

(10) $\sqrt{\dfrac{a}{b}-c^2}$ when $a=42$, $b=25$, and $c=0.75$

(11) $i\sqrt{\dfrac{a}{b}-\left(\dfrac{c}{b}\right)^2}$ when $a=489$, $b=50$, $c=-24$, $i=3$

(12) $\dfrac{a-bc}{\sqrt{1-b^2}\,\sqrt{1-c^2}}$ when $a=.35$, $b=.60$, $c=.80$

SECOND TEST

1. Find the results of carrying out the indicated operations.

(1) $(n-4r-6)-3(2r+2-5n-p)$

(2) $(c-3d-2)+2(5d-c+a+1)$

(3) $-2(6M_1+2M_2-M_3)$

(4) $(15c^2-20cd-18c^2d) \div (-10c)$

2. Place a check mark in front of each of the following which is *necessarily* a positive number no matter whether the letters themselves have positive or negative values.

(1) x	(7) $(-x)^4$	(13) $\sqrt{9x^2}$
(2) x^2	(8) xy	(14) $\sqrt[3]{x}$
(3) x^3	(9) $x+y+z$	(15) $\sqrt[3]{x^2}$
(4) $(x^2)^3$	(10) $x^2+y^2+z^2$	(16) xyz
(5) $(-x)^2$	(11) $x^3+y^3+z^3$	(17) $\sqrt{x^2y^2z^2}$
(6) $(-x)^3$	(12) $xy+xz+yz$	(18) $\sqrt[3]{x^2yz}$

3. In the following expressions, suppose that none of the variables has the value zero, although any or all of them may be negative. It follows that some of the expressions may be negative in value, or may be zero when positive and negative values exactly balance, while others can be only positive. Place a check mark in front of each expression for which zero is a possible value.

(1) $a+b+c+d$

(2) $\sqrt{a}+\sqrt{b}+\sqrt{c}+\sqrt{d}$

(3) $ab+ac+ad+bc+bd+cd$

(4) $a^2+b^2+c^2+d^2$

(5) $\sqrt{abc}+\sqrt{abd}+\sqrt{bcd}+\sqrt{abd}$

(6) $a^3+b^3+c^3+d^3$

IX

SIMPLE EQUATIONS

INITIAL TEST

Solve the equations at the left to obtain the values of the expressions at the right.

1. $\Sigma x' = Nc$ $c \quad = $ ―――――

2. $r_{12} = \dfrac{\Sigma x_1 x_2}{N\sigma_1\sigma_2}$ $\Sigma x_1 x_2 = $ ―――――

3. $\sigma_p = \left\{\dfrac{pq}{n}\right\}^{\frac{1}{2}}$ $pq \quad = $ ―――――

4. $\sigma_{x-y}^2 = \sigma_x^2 - 2r_{xy}\sigma_x\sigma_y + \sigma_y^2$ $r_{xy} \quad = $ ―――――

5. $\sigma_{1.2} = \sigma_1\sqrt{1 - r_{12}^2}$ $r_{12} \quad = $ ―――――

6. $1 - R_{1.23}^2 = (1 - r_{12}^2)(1 - r_{13.2}^2)$ $R_{1.23} = $ ―――――

7. $\sigma_{ax} = \sigma_x\sqrt{1 - E_{xy}^2}$ $\dfrac{\sigma_{ax}^2}{\sigma_x^2} = $ ―――――

8. $r_1 = \dfrac{ar_2}{1 + (a - 1)r_2}$ $r_2 \quad = $ ―――――

9. $\Sigma x'y' = \Sigma xy + Nc_x c_y$ $\dfrac{\Sigma xy}{N} = $ ―――――

10. $\dfrac{\sigma_1}{\sigma_2} = \dfrac{\sqrt{1 - R}}{\sqrt{1 - r}}$ $R \quad = $ ―――――

Practical Importance. In elementary statistical work the solution of complicated equations is almost never necessary. Such equations as arise in changing the form of a formula are usually first degree equations involving fractions.

Sets of linear equations, sometimes with many variables, arise continually in more advanced statistical work. No one would attempt their solution without a knowl-

73

edge of determinants, and determinants are beyond the scope of this book, both because they are seldom used in elementary courses in statistical method and because any one attacking a problem requiring the use of determinants would be likely to know the mathematics presented in this book. To discuss here the solution of simultaneous linear equations by the methods of addition and substitution presented in elementary algebra texts would be of little value, because when simultaneous equations occur in a statistical problem they are likely to have so many variables that these elementary methods are cumbersome and impractical. The person who needs to solve a system of simultaneous equations with more than two variables will do well to study the method of determinants.

Finding the roots of an equation of higher degree is not often called for even in advanced statistical work. It is often necessary to formulate such an equation, to represent one variable by an expression in which higher powers of another occur, but these equations are seldom reversible. A statistical equation set up to describe y in powers of x usually cannot be solved to give a statistical equation for x in terms of y. Here is one of the striking differences between statistical method and ordinary algebra. Consequently the methods for finding roots of equations of higher degree will not be included here.

Fundamental Principles. The solution of simple equations depends upon the following set of principles:

In any equation the equality is not destroyed if—

1. *The same amount is added to each member;*
2. *The same amount is subtracted from each member;*
3. *Each member is multiplied by the same amount;*
4. *Each member is divided by the same amount.*

In general it may also be said that the equality is not de-

stroyed if each member is raised to the same power, or if the
same root is taken of each member. This statement needs
qualification because of the fact that every number has two
different square roots, three different cube roots, etc.

These principles may be applied in any order as is illustrated below:

Example 1. Solve $\dfrac{3a}{2}-\dfrac{x}{3}+a=3$ for x.

If we apply principle 3, and multiply both members at
once by 6, we will eliminate the fractions and simplify the
work.

$9a-2x+6a=18$ (Both members multiplied by 6)

$\qquad -2x=18-15a$ (15a subtracted from both members)

$\qquad\quad x=\dfrac{18-15a}{-2}$ (Both members divided by -2)

$\qquad\quad x=\dfrac{15a}{2}-9$

Example 2. Solve $a=\sqrt{3b-2c}$ for c.

$\qquad a^2=3b-2c$ (Both members squared)

$a^2+2c=3b$ (2c added to both members)

$\qquad 2c=3b-a^2$ (a^2 subtracted from both members)

$\qquad\;\; c=\dfrac{3b-a^2}{2}$ (Both members divided by 2)

Example 3. Solve $1-a^2=(1-b^2)(1-c^2)$ for b.

$\dfrac{1-a^2}{1-c^2}=1-b^2$ (Dividing both sides by $\{1-c^2\}$)

$b^2+\dfrac{1-a^2}{1-c^2}=1$ (Adding b^2 to both sides)

$\qquad b^2=1-\dfrac{1-a^2}{1-c^2}$ {Subtracting $\dfrac{1-a^2}{1-c^2}$ from both sides)

$\qquad b^2=\dfrac{a^2-c^2}{1-c^2}$

$\qquad\;\; b=\pm\sqrt{\dfrac{a^2-c^2}{1-c^2}}$ (Taking square root of both sides)

Transposition. When a term occurring in one member of an equation is made to disappear either by adding it to or subtracting it from both members, it reappears in the other member with its sign changed. This is illustrated in the preceding examples. Taking advantage of this fact, we may make as many additions and subtractions as we please, all at one time, in an expeditious fashion, combining principles 1 and 2 into the single principle:

Any term may be transposed from one member of an equation to the other if its sign be changed.

Checking the Solution. A solution is correct if, and only if, the equation reduces to an identity when this value is substituted for the unknown in the original equation. Thus in Example 1 above, we have as a check:

$$\frac{3a}{2} - \frac{1}{3}\left(\frac{15a}{2} - 9\right) + a = 3$$

$$\frac{3a}{2} - \frac{5a}{2} + 3 + a = 3$$

$$-a + 3 + a = 3, \text{ which is an obvious identity.}$$

Answers to the exercises in the following list have been given in the key at the back of the book, but the student will gain much more if he checks his answers instead of referring to the key. In some of these exercises, where a numerical value of the unknown is required, that value can be found only approximately, and the check is therefore not perfect, but precise to any desired degree of approximation, depending on the number of figures retained in the answer.

EXERCISE 16

1. $\dfrac{a}{b} = \dfrac{1}{c}$ $c =$ ———

2. $\dfrac{x}{2} + \dfrac{x}{7} = x - 5$ $x =$ ———

3. $0.2x + 4 - 0.5x = 3.5x - 2.08$ $x =$ ———

4. $a = b\sqrt{c - d^2}$ $\qquad\qquad d = \underline{}$

5. $c = \sqrt{\dfrac{a}{N}}$ $\qquad\qquad N = \underline{}$

6. $0.36y = 0.24$ $\qquad\qquad y = \underline{}$

7. $ab = a_1(b_1^2 + c_1^2) + a_2(b_2^2 + c_2^2)$ $\qquad a_2 = \underline{}$

$\qquad\qquad\qquad\qquad\qquad\qquad\qquad\qquad c_2 = \underline{}$

8. $x = \dfrac{ay}{by - c + d}$ $\qquad\qquad y = \underline{}$

9. $4.5 = 2\,\dfrac{\left(\dfrac{x}{4} + 5x\right)}{0.8 - x}$ $\qquad\qquad x = \underline{}$

10. $A = \tfrac{1}{2}bh$ $\qquad\qquad h = \underline{}$

11. $3.6y - 0.03y + 5.6 = 2.3y + 3.06$ $\qquad y = \underline{}$

12. $0.42r + 3.1 - 0.06r = 1.68$ $\qquad r = \underline{}$

13. $1.7 = \dfrac{0.17t - 1.4}{2.3}$ $\qquad\qquad t = \underline{}$

14. $0.43a = \dfrac{14 - 3x}{3}$ $\qquad\qquad x = \underline{}$

15. $\dfrac{y - 6}{3} + \dfrac{y - 7}{5} = 0$ $\qquad\qquad y = \underline{}$

16. $\dfrac{x - 0.3}{2x + 0.15} = 7$ $\qquad\qquad x = \underline{}$

SECOND TEST

Solve the equations at the left to obtain the values of the expressions at the right.

1. $p = 0.6745\sigma$ $\qquad\qquad \sigma \qquad = \underline{}$

2. $x_1 = r_{12}\left(\dfrac{\sigma_1}{\sigma_2}\right)x_2$ $\qquad \dfrac{x_1}{\sigma_1} \qquad = \underline{}$

3. $\sigma = \sqrt{\dfrac{\Sigma x^2}{N}}$ $\qquad\qquad \Sigma x^2 \qquad = \underline{}$

4. $\sigma_{a+b}^2 = \sigma_a^2 + 2r_{ab}\sigma_a\sigma_b + \sigma_b^2$ $\qquad r_{ab} \qquad = \underline{}$

5. $R_{1.23} = \left(1 - \dfrac{\sigma_{1.23}^2}{\sigma_1^2}\right)^{\frac{1}{2}}$ $\qquad \sigma_{1.23} \qquad = \underline{}$

6. $\sigma_{x \cdot y} = \sigma_x\sqrt{1 - r_{xy}^2}$ $\qquad 1 - \dfrac{\sigma_{x \cdot y}^2}{\sigma_z^2} \qquad = \underline{}$

7. $N_T \sigma_T^2 = N_1(\sigma_1^2 + d_1^2) + N_2(\sigma_2^2 + d_2^2)$ σ_1 = ———

8. $r_1 = \dfrac{r_2}{a - r_2(a-1)}$ r_2 = ———

9. $\Sigma(x')^2 = \Sigma x^2 + Nc^2$ $\dfrac{\Sigma x^2}{N}$ = ———

10. $\dfrac{\sqrt{1-r_1}}{\sqrt{1-r_2}} = \dfrac{S_2}{S_1}$ r_2 = ———

X

FRACTIONS

Initial Test

After taking the test, compare your answers with the key. If you have made any errors, study the practice material and take the second test.

1. Place a plus sign before each statement which you believe to be correct and a zero before each statement which you believe to be incorrect.

(1) $\dfrac{a}{b}+c=\dfrac{a+c}{b}$

(2) $\dfrac{a}{b}=\dfrac{ma}{mb}$

(3) $\dfrac{a}{b}=\dfrac{a+m}{b+m}$

(4) $\dfrac{12}{1}=12$

(5) $\dfrac{0.5b}{1.5c}=\dfrac{b}{3c}$

(6) $\dfrac{ab+x}{b}=a+x$

(7) $\dfrac{0.0055}{0.0077}=\dfrac{5}{7}$

(8) $\dfrac{0}{4}=\dfrac{0}{7}$

(9) $\dfrac{a}{x}+1=\dfrac{a+1}{x}$

(10) $\dfrac{14}{0}=0$

(11) $1-\dfrac{a-b}{c}=\dfrac{c-a-b}{c}$

(12) $1\div\dfrac{3}{8}=\dfrac{8}{3}$

(13) $\dfrac{0.04}{0.06}=\dfrac{2}{3}$

(14) $\dfrac{6}{0.1}=0.6$

(15) $\dfrac{b}{c}+\dfrac{d}{a}=\dfrac{b+d}{a+c}$

(16) $\dfrac{x}{y}-\dfrac{y}{x}=\dfrac{x^2-y^2}{xy}$

(17) $\dfrac{0}{2}\times\dfrac{3}{4}=0$

(18) $\dfrac{a(a-b)-a^2}{b}=-a$

(19) $\dfrac{25}{0}=25$

(20) $\dfrac{2}{3}\div\dfrac{5}{6}=\dfrac{4}{5}$

(21) $\dfrac{a}{x}=\dfrac{a^2}{x^2}$

(22) $\dfrac{n^2-4n}{3n}=\dfrac{n-4}{3}$

(23) $\dfrac{x^2+2x+4}{x^2+a+4}=\dfrac{2x}{a}$

(24) $\dfrac{c}{d}\cdot\dfrac{d}{c}=0$

2. $a = \dfrac{bx}{c}$. Solve this for x.

3. $r_x = \dfrac{nr_1}{1+(n-1)r_1}$. Solve this for r_1.

4. $x = \dfrac{an-c}{b-c}$. Find n if $a = \frac{3}{4}$, $b = 1\frac{5}{6}$, $c = \frac{2}{3}$, $x = 5$.

5. Underscore each response that is correct:

In the formula $\qquad S = \dfrac{1-r^2}{\sqrt{N}}$

(1) If N increases and r is constant, S tends to increase, decrease, remain constant.

(2) If r increases in absolute value and N is constant, S tends to increase, decrease, remain constant.

(3) If $r = 0$, and N is larger than 1, S will be 0, 1, a fraction smaller than one, a number larger than one, a positive number, a negative number, sometimes positive and sometimes negative.

(4) If $r = 1$, and N is larger than 1, S will be 0, 1, a fraction smaller than one, a number larger than one, a positive number, a negative number, sometimes positive and sometimes negative.

(5) If r is a fraction smaller than 1 and N is larger than 1, S will be 0, 1, a fraction smaller than one, a number larger than one, a positive number, a negative number, sometimes positive and sometimes negative.

(6) If r is a number larger than 1 and N is a number larger than 1, S will be 0, 1, a fraction smaller than one, a number larger than one, a positive number, a negative number, sometimes positive and sometimes negative.

Practical Importance. Statistical computation continually involves complex fractions and fractional expressions appearing under a square root sign. Statistical formulas are unnecessarily alarming to the person not conversant with the laws of fractions. The student who cannot manipulate algebraic fractions wonders why the textbooks seem to give a large number of different formulas for such a measure as the coefficient of correlation. He is obliged to impress upon his memory many formulas which seem to him diverse and independent and which he frequently confuses. The student who is at home in the algebraic manipulation of fractions recognizes that these are but variants of a single formula. He memorizes this basic formula and passes easily to its modifications when need arises.

Change in Form of a Fraction. The fundamental principle in all work with fractions is: *Multiplying or dividing the numerator and the denominator of a fraction by the same number does not change the value of the fraction.* In symbolic form this rule might be stated as

$$\frac{a}{b} = \frac{na}{nb}, \quad \text{or} \quad a/b = na/nb$$

$$\text{and} \ \frac{a}{b} = \frac{a/n}{b/n} \quad \text{or} \quad a/b = (a/n) \ / \ (b/n)$$

This principle is employed to reduce fractions to simpler forms.

$\dfrac{675}{825} = \dfrac{9}{11}.$ Both terms were divided by 75.

$\dfrac{0.0525}{0.0925} = \dfrac{21}{37}.$ Both terms were multiplied by 400.

$\dfrac{\dfrac{27}{18} - \left(\dfrac{25}{6}\right)\left(\dfrac{13}{2}\right)}{\dfrac{11}{12} - \left(\dfrac{5}{9}\right)\left(\dfrac{1}{2}\right)} = \dfrac{54 - 3(25)(13)}{33 - 2(5)(1)} = \dfrac{-921}{23}.$ Both numerator and denominator were multiplied by 36.

$\dfrac{\dfrac{a}{N} - \dfrac{bc}{N^2}}{\sqrt{\dfrac{e}{N} - \dfrac{b^2}{N^2}} \sqrt{\dfrac{d}{N} - \dfrac{c^2}{N^2}}} = \dfrac{Na - bc}{\sqrt{Ne - b^2}\sqrt{Nd - c^2}}.$ This is the general form of the formula for the coefficient

of correlation. The numerator was multiplied by N^2. Each factor in the denominator was multiplied by N, which multiplied the entire denominator by N^2, and thus kept the value of the fraction unchanged. To see how each factor in the denominator was multiplied by N, study the following:

$$(N) \sqrt{\frac{e}{N} - \frac{b^2}{N^2}} = (\sqrt{N^2}) \sqrt{\frac{e}{N} - \frac{b^2}{N^2}}$$

$$= \sqrt{(N^2)\left(\frac{e}{N} - \frac{b^2}{N^2}\right)} = \sqrt{Ne - b^2}$$

Similarly the second factor of the denominator becomes $\sqrt{Nd - c^2}$. For further help on the multiplication of radicals, see Chapter XII.

Cautions. There are several pitfalls into which the unwary may fall:

1. In general, to *add* the same number to the numerator and denominator of a fraction, changes the value of the fraction.

$$\frac{3}{4} \text{ is not equal to } \frac{3+5}{4+5}, \text{ or } \frac{8}{9}$$

$$\frac{a}{b} \text{ is not equal to } \frac{a+n}{b+n}, \text{ or to } \frac{a-n}{b-n}$$

$$\text{unless } a = b \quad \text{or} \quad n = 0.$$

Even though one knows this general principle, there is often a temptation hastily to strike out part of the numerator and denominator of a fraction by careless cancellation, as

$$\frac{a^2 + 5a + 3}{b^2 + 2b + 3}$$

This is of course entirely wrong, and results from haste or from working mechanically without an understanding of the process.

2. In general, squaring a fraction or taking its square root changes its value.

$$\frac{2}{3} \text{ is not equal to } \left(\frac{2}{3}\right)^2, \text{ which is } \frac{4}{9}$$

$$\frac{a}{b} \text{ is not equal to } \left(\frac{a}{b}\right)^2, \text{ which is } \frac{a^2}{b^2}$$

3. There is a common temptation to forget that the bar of a fraction acts as a parenthesis. When several fractions having a common denominator are to be added, if a minus sign stands in front of any one of them, the signs of *all* the terms in the numerator of that fraction must be changed before the numerators can be added. Carelessness here is a fruitful source of error in dealing with fractions. Thus

$$a - \frac{x-1}{2} = \frac{2a}{2} - \frac{x-1}{2} = \frac{2a-(x-1)}{2} = \frac{2a-x+1}{2}, \text{ not } \frac{2a-x-1}{2}$$

Equality of Two Fractions. A second principle of fundamental importance in dealing with fractions is: *If two fractions are equal, and their denominators are equal, then their numerators must be equal, and vice versa.* This principle is useful in solving fractional equations.

Thus if $\frac{7}{x} = \frac{7}{15}$, it must be that $x = 15$.

If $\frac{5(x-1)}{7} = \frac{3}{14}$, then $\frac{10(x-1)}{14} = \frac{3}{14}$,

and therefore $10(x-1) = 3$.

If $\frac{6}{3x+2} = \frac{3}{4}$, then $\frac{6}{3x+2} = \frac{6}{8}$, and therefore $3x+2 = 8$.

Product of Fractions. The product of two fractions is a new fraction whose numerator is the product of their numerators and whose denominator is the product of their denominators. Thus

$$\left(\frac{4}{9}\right) \times \left(\frac{3}{8}\right) = \frac{4 \times 3}{9 \times 8} = \frac{12}{72} = \frac{1}{6}$$

Often the process of multiplication may be shortened by dividing out factors which are common to any numerator and any denominator before the multiplication rather than after it. In the example just given we might have saved time by dividing the first numerator and the second denominator each by 4, and dividing the second numerator and the first denominator each by 3.

Division by a Fraction. To find the quotient of a number by a fraction, we invert the fraction and proceed as in multiplication. This rule is only a special aspect of our first principle. If we multiply both terms of $\dfrac{a}{b/c}$ by $\dfrac{c}{b}$ the numerator becomes $a\left(\dfrac{c}{b}\right)$ and the denominator becomes 1. Therefore $a \div \left(\dfrac{b}{c}\right) = a\left(\dfrac{c}{b}\right)$

Addition or Subtraction of Fractions. To add two fractions we first change them to equivalent fractions having a common denominator, then their sum is a fraction whose numerator is the sum of the numerators of the equivalent fractions and whose denominator is the common denominator.

For example, $\dfrac{7}{25} + \dfrac{3}{2} = \dfrac{14}{50} + \dfrac{75}{50} = \dfrac{89}{50}$

$$\frac{x+y}{c} - \frac{1}{2} = \frac{2x+2y}{2c} - \frac{c}{2c} = \frac{2x+2y-c}{2c}$$

Notice that subtraction is only a special case of addition.

Zero in a Denominator. The use of fractions with zero as denominator is not permissible. Division by zero occurs in a problem in elementary statistics only when a blunder has been made. A student who did not understand what are significant digits might round off the numbers in such a

fraction as $\dfrac{0.061}{0.002}$ to $\dfrac{0.06}{0.00}$, thus incorrectly seeming to produce a division by zero.

To say that $\dfrac{5}{0} = x$ is equivalent to saying $0x = 5$, or "What
number can be multiplied by zero to produce 5?" Since the
product of zero and any finite number is 0, there is no finite
number x which equal to $\dfrac{5}{0}$.

EXERCISE 17

1. (a) $\frac{2}{3} + \frac{4}{5} = ?$ (c) $\frac{4}{7} + \frac{2}{3} = ?$ (e) $\frac{2}{9} + \frac{3}{7} = ?$
   (b) $\frac{3}{8} + \frac{1}{3} = ?$ (d) $\frac{3}{2} + \frac{5}{4} = ?$ (f) $\frac{2}{3} + \frac{5}{6} = ?$

2. Write a formula to state in symbolic language a rule for adding
   any two fractions.

3. (a) $(\frac{2}{3})(\frac{4}{5}) = ?$ (c) $(\frac{4}{7})(\frac{2}{3}) = ?$ (e) $(\frac{2}{9})(\frac{3}{7}) = ?$
   (b) $(\frac{3}{8})(\frac{1}{3}) = ?$ (d) $(\frac{3}{2})(\frac{5}{4}) = ?$ (f) $(\frac{2}{3})(\frac{5}{6}) = ?$

4. Write a formula to state in symbolic language a rule for multiplying any two fractions.

5. (a) $\frac{2}{3} \div \frac{4}{5} = ?$ (c) $\frac{4}{7} \div \frac{2}{3} = ?$ (e) $\frac{2}{9} \div \frac{3}{7} = ?$
   (b) $\frac{3}{8} \div \frac{1}{3} = ?$ (d) $\frac{3}{2} \div \frac{5}{4} = ?$ (f) $\frac{2}{3} \div \frac{5}{6} = ?$

6. Write a formula to state in symbolic language a rule for dividing
   one fraction by another.

7. (1) If both terms of the fraction $\frac{3}{4}$ are multiplied by 5, the result
   is —————— and this value is (just as large, 5 times as
   large, $\frac{1}{5}$ as large) as the original fraction.
   (2) If the numerator of the fraction $\frac{2}{3}$ is multiplied by 5, the
   result is —————— and this value is (just as large, 5 times
   as large, $\frac{1}{5}$ as large) as the original fraction.
   (3) If the denominator of the fraction $\frac{2}{3}$ is multiplied by 5,
   the result is —————— and this value is (just as large,
   5 times as large, $\frac{1}{5}$ as large) as the original fraction.

(4) If the fraction $\frac{2}{3}$ is multiplied by 5, the result is ———— and this value is (just as large, 5 times as large, $\frac{1}{5}$ as large) as the original fraction.

(5) If both terms of the fraction $\frac{a}{b}$ are multiplied by c, the result is ———— and this value is (just as large, c times as large, $\frac{1}{c}$ times as large) as the original fraction.

(6) If the fraction $\frac{a}{b}$ is multiplied by c, the result is ———— and this value is (just as large, c times as large, $\frac{1}{c}$ times as large) as the original fraction.

(7) If the fraction $\frac{a}{b}$ is squared, the result is ———— and this value is (just as large, $\frac{a}{b}$ times as large, $\frac{b}{a}$ times as large) as the original fraction.

8. If $\dfrac{a(b+c)}{d}=e$, solve for b.

Suggestions: First multiply both sides of the equation by d. Then divide both sides by a. Then subtract c from both sides.

9. If $a=\dfrac{bc}{1+(b-1)c}$, solve for c.

Suggestions: First multiply both sides of the equation by the denominator of the fraction. Get all the terms containing c into one side of the equation and all other terms into the other side. Express the terms containing c as the product of c and some expression of several terms. Divide both sides of the equation by some expression which will leave c alone on that side of the equation.

10. If $r_x = \dfrac{nr_1}{1+(n-1)r_1}$, find r_x when

   (1) $n=2$ and $r_1=.70$

   (2) $n=3$ and $r_1=.67$

   (3) $n=4$ and $r_1=.85$

   (4) $n=3$ and $r_1=.92$

11. If $r_x = \dfrac{nr_1}{1+(n-1)r_1}$, find r_1 when

   (1) $n=2$ and $r_x=.86$

   (2) $n=4$ and $r_x=.97$

   (3) $n=3$ and $r_x=.91$

12. $p = \dfrac{a(b-c)}{d}$.

   (1) Find p if $a=\frac{1}{2}$, $b=\frac{2}{3}$, $c=\frac{1}{6}$, and $d=\frac{3}{4}$.

   (2) If a is multiplied by 3, but b, c, and d are not changed, what would be the value of p?

   (3) If d is multiplied by 3, but a, b, and c are not changed, what would be the value of p?

   (4) If b is multiplied by 3, but a, b, and d are not changed, what would be the value of p?

   (5) If c is multiplied by 5, but a, b, and d are not changed, what would be the value of p? If c is multiplied by 2? By 4?

   (6) What is the general effect on p of an increase in a? An increase in b? An increase in c? An increase in d?

SECOND TEST

1. Place a plus sign before each statement which you believe to be correct and a zero before each statement which you believe to be incorrect.

   (1) $\dfrac{n+x}{n}=1+\dfrac{x}{n}$ (3) $\dfrac{p+q}{p+r}=\dfrac{q}{r}$

   (2) $\dfrac{pq}{pr}=\dfrac{q}{r}$ (4) $\dfrac{c}{1}=c$

(5) $\dfrac{0.07a}{0.21x} = \dfrac{a}{3x}$

(15) $\dfrac{a}{x} + \dfrac{a}{y} = \dfrac{2a}{xy}$

(6) $\dfrac{cn+a}{c} = n+a$

(16) $\dfrac{a}{b} - \dfrac{b}{a} = \dfrac{a^2-b^2}{ab}$

(7) $\dfrac{0}{3} = \dfrac{0}{300}$

(17) $\dfrac{3}{2} \times \dfrac{0}{6} \times \dfrac{1}{3} = 0$

(8) $\dfrac{1.8r}{0.3r} = 6$

(18) $\dfrac{a}{x} \cdot \dfrac{x}{a} = 0$

(9) $\dfrac{0.0027}{0.009} = 0.3$

(19) $\dfrac{c(c-x)-c^2}{c} = -x$

(10) $\dfrac{x}{0} = 0$

(20) $\dfrac{n}{0} = n$

(11) $a - \dfrac{x-3a}{4} = \dfrac{a-x}{4}$

(21) $\dfrac{a}{x} \div \dfrac{x}{y} = \dfrac{a}{y}$

(12) $1 \div \dfrac{c}{d} = \dfrac{d}{c}$

(22) $\dfrac{n}{m} = \dfrac{n^2}{m^2}$

(13) $\dfrac{7}{12} \div \dfrac{1}{12} = 7$

(23) $\dfrac{ax+x^2}{x} = a+x$

(14) $\dfrac{150}{0.2} = 7.5$

(24) $\dfrac{p+3}{pq+3} = \dfrac{1}{q}$

2. $M_T = \dfrac{N_1 M_1 + N_2 M_2}{N_T}$. Solve for M_1.

3. $r_1 = \dfrac{r_2}{n-(n-1)r_2}$. Solve for r_2.

4. $x = \dfrac{bc-d}{b-d}$. Find b if $c = \dfrac{3}{7}$, $d = \dfrac{1}{12}$, $x = \dfrac{3}{11}$.

5. Underscore each response that is correct.

In the formula $r = \dfrac{Na-bc}{\sqrt{e-b^2}\,\sqrt{f-c^2}}$ in which N is positive,

(1) If a increases and all other values in the right hand member do not change, r will increase, decrease, remain unaffected.

(2) If f increases and all other values in the right hand member do not change, r will increase, decrease, remain unaffected.

(3) If b is a negative number and all the other numbers are positive, and if b^2 is less than e and c^2 less than f, r will be positive, negative, uncertain as to sign.

5. In the formula $R = \sqrt{1 - \dfrac{s^2}{a^2}}$,

(1) If $s = a$ and a is not zero, R will be 0, 1, a fraction smaller than one, a number larger than one, a number which may be either larger or smaller than one, the square root of a negative number.

(2) If s is smaller than a in absolute value, R will be 0, 1, a fraction smaller than one, a number larger than one, a number which may be either larger or smaller than one, the square root of a negative number.

(3) If s is zero and a is not zero, R will be 0, 1, a fraction smaller than one, a number larger than one, a number which may be either larger or smaller than one, the square root of a negative number.

XI

GRAPHS

Initial Test

1. Below is a list of equations and a list of phrases. Select all the equations which are correctly described by the first phrase. Write the numbers of *all* such equations on the line at the right of this phrase. Do the same for each of the other phrases in the list.

   a. An equation whose graph would pass through the origin. _____

   b. An equation whose graph is not a straight line. _____

   c. An equation whose graph is a straight line parallel to the graph of $y = 3x + 4$. _____

   d. An equation whose graph is a straight line passing through the origin and lying in the second and fourth quadrants. _____

   e. An equation whose graph cuts the y-axis 3 units above the origin. _____

   f. An equation whose graph is a straight line parallel to the x-axis. _____

   g. An equation whose graph is a straight line passing through the origin and lying nearer to the x-axis than to the y-axis. _____

(1) $x = -4y$	(5) $xy = 4$	(8) $y = 2x^2 + 3x$
(2) $y = x^2 - 2x + 3$	(6) $3y = x$	(9) $x^2 + y^2 = 25$
(3) $y = 3x - 2$	(7) $y = 3x$	(10) $x + y = 3$
(4) $y = 3$		

2. Make a graph of the straight line which passes through the points $(1, 4)$ and $(3, 7)$ and find its equation.

3. Write the equation of the straight line which:

90

(1) Crosses the y-axis 2 points above the origin and has a slope of $+5$.

(2) Crosses the y-axis at the origin and has a slope of $-\frac{4}{5}$.

4. On the same set of axes, make graphs of the two equations $\begin{cases} 2x-3y=5 \\ 3x-5y=7 \end{cases}$ and find the coördinates of the point at which they intersect.

Importance. Knowledge of how to make and how to read simple mathematical graphs greatly facilitates the construction and interpretation of statistical graphs. The inverse operation of finding the equation for a line already drawn is essential to the analysis of many statistical problems, and particularly important for a clear understanding of correlation and regression. For these purposes there is needed a somewhat more dynamic appreciation of functional relationships than is usually acquired by the student who has learned only to plot isolated points and to connect these by a line.

Graphic Representation of Single Numbers. A single number can be represented by a point on a linear scale, such as the scale of which Figure 1 shows a small portion. Here the point A represents approximately the number 2.3, B the number $-.4$, C the number -4.7, and D the number 5.5.

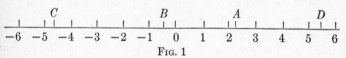

FIG. 1

EXERCISE 18

1. On the number scale shown in Figure 1, locate the points 2, $3\frac{1}{2}$, $2\frac{1}{3}$, -3, $-1\frac{1}{4}$, $\frac{2}{3}$, $-\frac{3}{4}$, $-5\frac{1}{4}$.

2. Locate the point midway between 1 and 4. What number corresponds to it? What number corresponds to a point midway

between −3 and −1? Midway between −3 and +2? Midway between −½ and +5?

3. What number corresponds to a point 2 units to the left of the point −1? Three units to the right of −2? Four units to the right of 2? Three units to the left of 4? One unit to the left of −3?

4. What number corresponds to a point *a* units to the right of the point 2? *b* units to the left of −3? *c* units to the right of −1? *d* units to the left of 4?

5. Make a rough sketch of a thermometer, indicating degrees above zero by plus signs and degrees below zero by minus signs. What is the value of the point midway between +15° and +43°? Midway between −6° and +8°? Five degrees above −7°? Six degrees below +2°? Twenty degrees above −9°?

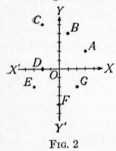

Graphic Representation of Pairs of Numbers. Suppose that Figure 2 represents a portion of a map on which *X′X* is a road extending east and *Y′Y* is a road extending north through *O*. A scale of miles is marked off along each road.

Fig. 2   Exercise 19

1. Verify the following statements by a study of the map.

The point *A* is 3 miles east and 2 miles north of *O*. It may be designated as (3, 2).

The point *B* is 1 mile east and 4 miles north of *O*. It may be designated as (1, 4).

The point *C* is 2 miles west and 5 miles north of *O*. It may be designated as (−2, 5).

The point *D* is 2 miles west and 0 miles north of *O*. It may be designated as (−2, 0).

The point *E* is 3 miles west and 2 miles south of *O*. It may be designated as (−3, −2).

The point F is 0 miles west and 4 miles south of O. It may be
designated as $(0, -4)$.
The point G is 2 miles east and 2 miles south of O. It may be
designated as $(2, -2)$.

2. Notice that in problem 1 each point was described by two numbers enclosed in a parenthesis. The first of these numbers represents the distance east or west from O, distances east being positive and distances west negative. The second number represents
the distance north or south from O, distances north being positive and distances south negative. Complete the following
sentences by writing the words *north*, *south*, *east*, and *west* in the
blank spaces.

(1) The point $(4, 2)$ would be 4 miles ———— and 2 miles ————
   of O.
(2) The point $(-3, -5)$ would be 3 miles ———— and 5 miles
   ———— of O.
(3) The point $(7, -1)$ would be 7 miles ———— and 1 mile ————
   of O.
(4) The point $(-6, 2)$ would be 6 miles ———— and 2 miles ————
   of O.

In a mathematical graph, the point O is known as the
origin. The lines XX' and YY' are respectively the x-axis
and the y-axis, and together are called
the *coördinate axes*. These lines divide
the plane into four parts known as
quadrants, which are designated by
numbers as shown in Figure 3. The distance to a point from the x-axis is
called the *ordinate* of the point. The
distance to the point from the y-axis
is called its *abscissa*. The ordinate and

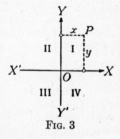

Fig. 3

abscissa together are called the *coördinates* of the point. Abscissas are customarily denoted by the letter x and ordinates

by the letter y, as in Figure 3. When a point is designated by a pair of numbers, as in the two preceding examples, the x-coördinate or abscissa is given first.

3. Write one word on each blank line to complete the sentence.

(1) The ordinate of any point is the length of a line extending to that point from the ——— axis and parallel to the ——— axis.

(2) The x-value of a point is measured along a line parallel to the ——— axis and perpendicular to the ——— axis.

(3) The y-value of a point is measured along a line parallel to the ——— axis and perpendicular to the ——— axis.

(4) In quadrant I, all abscissas are ——— and all ordinates ———.

(5) In quadrant II, all abscissas are ——— and all ordinates ———.

(6) In quadrant III, all abscissas are ——— and all ordinates ———.

(7) In quadrant IV, all abscissas are ——— and all ordinates ———.

(8) If both coördinates of a point are negative, it must lie in quadrant ———.

(9) If the two coördinates of a point have the same sign, it must lie in either quadrant ——— or quadrant ———.

(10) If a point lies on the x-axis, its ——— is zero while its ——— may have any value.

(11) If a point lies on the y-axis, its ——— is zero while its ——— may have any value.

(12) If a point lies nearer to the x-axis than to the y-axis, its ——— is larger than its ———.

(13) If a point lies nearer to the vertical axis than to the horizontal, its ——— is larger than its ———.

4. On a sheet of coördinate paper draw coördinate axes and plot each of the following points, marking its position with a small dot and writing the name of the point, as (3, 5) beside the dot:

$$(3, 5) \qquad (1, -3) \qquad (6, 0) \qquad (-2, 2)$$

Verify your plotting by noting that these four points are the four corners of a square. If the points you have marked do not indicate a square, one or more of them must be in error.

5. On coördinate axes plot the following points:

(0, 3)	(0, −1)	(1, 0)	(−8, −6)	(−2, −3)
(−4, 1)	(−14, −9)	(8, 7)	(−5, 0)	(4, 3)
(−7, −2)	(−11, −6)	(−10, −7)	(−4, −4)	

To provide an easy check on the accuracy of your plotting, these points have been chosen so that they lie on a quadrilateral whose vertices are at (−4, 1), (8, 7), (−2, −3), and (−14, −9).

Graph of an Equation.   Consider that Figure 2 represents a portion of a map cut by two crossroads intersecting at right angles. Mark the path over which you would travel if you should move in such a way as to be always two miles west of OY. Translating into algebraic language the condition that your position is always 2 miles west of OY, we have $x = −2$. The path you would follow is a line parallel to and two units to the left of OY. Drawing this line and writing $x = −2$ are two different ways of expressing the same relationship. Therefore we call the line you have drawn the graph of the equation.   The graph and the equation state the same facts, but state them in different ways.

Exercise 20

1. Mark the path along which you would travel if you should start at O and walk in such a way that at any moment you are just as far from OX as from OY.

    (1) Mark the path you follow if you walk only in quadrants I and III.

    (2) Mark the path you follow if you walk only in quadrants II and IV.

2. Write an equation to describe the conditions in Question 1. In each case we wish to say in algebraic language that x and y

are numerically equal. In quadrants I and III, x and y have the same signs, so the equation is $x=y$ or $x-y=0$. Reference to the path marked in Question **1** shows that the graph passes through O and extends due northeast and southwest, that is, bisecting the angle between OX and OY. Write the equation directly on its graph.

In quadrants II and IV, x and y have opposite signs, so the equation is $x=-y$ or $x+y=0$. Reference to the drawing shows that the graph passes through O and extends due northwest and southeast. Write the equation directly on the graph.

3. Imagine that you start from O and walk in either quadrant I or quadrant III in such a way that at any moment you are just twice as far from OX as from OY. Mark the path along which you would travel. Write an equation to describe your path.

4. Imagine that you start from O and walk in either quadrant II or quadrant IV in such a way that at any moment you are three times as far from OY as from OX. Mark the path along which you would travel. Write an equation to describe your path.

5. Imagine that you are walking across country in such a way that the sum of your distance from OY and your distance from OX is always 5 miles. At what point would you cross OY? At what point would you cross OX? Mark the path along which you would travel. State the equation which expresses the condition of this problem. How many pairs of numbers are there which satisfy this equation? May the line you have drawn be extended indefinitely far in both directions?

6. Plot the points whose coördinates have the following pairs of values:

x	-4	-2	0	2	4	6			
y	-2	-1	0	1	2	3			

What position do these points take with respect to each other? Study the pairs of numbers to discern a relation between x and

y which holds for all the pairs. State this relation in an equation.

Write three more pairs of coördinates for which this relation would be true.

Plot these three additional points.

7. Plot the points whose coördinates have the following values:

x	4	1	-1	10	-5	5			
y	3	6	8	-3	12	2			

What position do these points take with respect to each other?

Study the pairs of numbers to discover a relation between x and y which holds for all the pairs. State this relation in an equation.

Write three more pairs of coördinates which satisfy this equation.

Plot these three additional points.

8. Fill in the blank squares below so as to have five pairs of coördinates for which the relation $y = x + 2$ shall be true.

x	-2	-1	0	1	2	3
y						

Plot the points and see what position they take with respect to each other.

9. Fill in the blank squares below so as to have six pairs of coördinates for which the relation $y = 2x + 3$ shall be true.

x	1		0		-2	
y		1		0		4

With a ruler draw a line through any two of the six points. Does the line pass through the other four points?

How many points are *necessary* to determine a graph when it is a straight line?

Note the advantage of plotting three points so that the third may
serve as a check on the accuracy of the other two.

In this problem did it seem easier to find values of y corresponding to a given value of x or to find values of x corresponding to
a given value of y? Why? Can you use this observation as a
principle of economy for saving time in later work?

10. Fill in the blank squares below so as to have nine pairs of co-
ordinates for which the relation $y = x^2$ shall be true.

x	-3	-2	-1	$-\frac{1}{2}$	0	$\frac{1}{2}$	3		
y	9	4							

Do these points lie on a straight line?

In what respect does this equation differ from the equations
you have previously studied whose graphs were straight lines?
Draw a smooth curve through these points.

11. Fill in the blank spaces below so as to have eight pairs of co-
ordinates for which the relation $y = 2x^2 - 3x + 5$ shall be true.

x	-1	0	$\frac{1}{2}$	$\frac{3}{4}$	1	2	3	
y								

Plot the points and draw a smooth curve through them.

(This curve and the one drawn in **10** are called *parabolas*.)

12. Make a graph of $2y - 5x = 4$.

Make a graph of $y = \frac{5}{2}x + 2$.

While the two equations are equivalent and have exactly the
same graph, the second is easier to deal with. This is known as
the "standard form" of an equation. Before graphing an equation it is usually economical to reduce it to standard form by
rearranging terms so that the y terms are in the left hand
member and all others in the right, then dividing both members
by the coefficient of y. Values are then assigned to x and the
corresponding values found for y to secure number pairs for
plotting.

Rewrite the following equations in standard form.

(1) $3y - 2x = 7$

(2) $4y - 3x = x^2 + 8$

(3) $2x - 5y = 10$

(4) $x + 5y = 50$

(5) $7y + 2x - 20 = 0$

(6) $2y - 3x = 6$

(7) $x - y = 5$

(8) $2y = x^2 + 4x - 12$

(9) $3x = 2y + 10$

(10) $4 = 3x - 5y$

(11) $ay = bx + c$

(12) $cy + dx = k$

13. Make a graph of each of the following equations, using the method of Questions 6 to 11 to find the numerical values of the coördinates of selected points. These equations are arranged in groups to enable you to study the relation of the lines in each group and thus to discover for yourself certain general principles. Plot the equations in the first group all on one pair of axes and study the result to see what generalizations you can make concerning the form of the equation and the position of its graph. Then plot the equations of the second group on a second pair of axes, and so on. When all are drawn, study the charts thus made to find the answers to the questions in the next paragraph.

(1) $y = 2x$
$y = 2x + 2$
$y = 2x + 5$
$y = 2x - 3$
$y = 2x - 6$

(2) $x + y = 0$
$x - y = 0$
$x + y = 5$
$x - y = 5$

(3) $y = x^2$
$y = x^2 + 6$
$y = x^2 - 4$

(4) $y = x^2 + 2x$
$y = x^2 + 2x + 10$
$y = x^2 + 2x - 8$

(5) $2x + 3y = 0$
$2x + 3y = 6$
$2x + 3y = 10$
$2x + 3y = -5$

(6) $y = 3x$
$x = 3y$
$y = -3x$
$x = -3y$

14. Study the charts drawn for Question 13 to find the answers to these questions:

(1) If a graph passes through the origin, how does its equation differ from the equation of a graph which does not pass through the origin?

(2) What is the difference between the equation of a straight line graph and that of a graph which is not a straight line?

(3) What are the distinguishing characteristics of the equations of a set of parallel lines such as those in groups 1 and 5?

(4) When a linear equation is written in standard form, what indicates its slope? (Note that a set of parallel lines have the same slope.)

(5) When an equation is written in standard form, what indicates the point at which it crosses the y-axis?

(6) Suppose that $y = mx + b$ is a general formula for a linear equation in standard form. What does m show concerning the graph? What does b show?

(7) What is the difference between the equations of straight line graphs which have a general northeast-southwest direction and the equations of straight line graphs which have a general southeast-northwest direction? Study the graphs in groups 2 and 6. Put the equations all into standard form before you make comparisons.

15. Plot the line $4y - 3x = 6$, as in Figure 4. Choose any two points

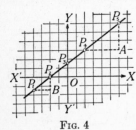

on this line, as P_4 and P_5 and find their coördinates. From P_4 draw a line parallel to OX and from P_5 a line parallel to OY, and let these lines meet at a point which we will call A. (Two letters used to describe a line segment, as OX, AP_5, P_4A, etc., indicate the ends of that segment and do not imply multiplication of two numbers as in the ordinary algebraic symbolism.)

Fig. 4

Then the *slope of the line* is

$$\frac{AP_5}{P_4A} = \frac{(y_5 - y_4)}{(x_5 - x_4)} = \frac{3}{4}.$$

As a check select any other two points on the same line, for example $P_1 = (-4, -1\frac{1}{2})$ and $P_2 = (-2, 0)$ and proceed in the same way.

$$\text{Slope} = \frac{BP_2}{P_1B} = \frac{1\frac{1}{2}}{2} = \frac{3}{4}.$$

Note that the slope is very easily obtained from the coördinates of the points where the line cuts the two axes.

$$\frac{OP_3}{P_2O} = \frac{1\frac{1}{2}}{2} = \frac{3}{4}.$$

Rewrite the equation in standard form, obtaining $y = \frac{3}{4}x + 1\frac{1}{2}$. Notice that when the equation is in this form, the coefficient of x gives the slope of the line and the constant term gives the ordinate of the point at which the line cuts the y-axis. The slope shows the increase in y which accompanies a unit increase in x. In this case, for every unit increase in x, there is $\frac{3}{4}$ of a unit increase in y.

16. Rewrite the equation $5y + 2x = 20$ in standard form. At what point will the graph of this equation cut the vertical axis? On coördinate paper lay off two perpendicular axes and mark the point $(0, 4)$.

How many units will y change for every unit of change in x? If x increases will y increase or decrease? What is the slope of this line?

Obviously the line crosses the vertical axis 4 units above the origin. Since its slope is $-\frac{2}{5}$, there must be $\frac{2}{5}$ of a unit decrease in y for every unit increase in x. After marking the point $(0, 4)$ we may locate another point 1 unit to the right of this and $\frac{2}{5}$ unit below it, and may draw a line through these two points. However, since greater accuracy can be achieved by the use of points farther apart, we may take our second point 10 units to the right of $(0, 4)$ and $\frac{2}{5} \times 10 = 4$ units below it, or we may use a point 5 units *to the left* and $\frac{2}{5} \times 5 = 2$ units *above* it, or any other point found in the same way.

17. In similar fashion, draw the graphs of

$$
\begin{aligned}
&(1)\ 2x + 3y = 15 \\
&(2)\ \tfrac{1}{2}y - 5x = 6 \\
&(3)\ 7y + 3x = 0 \\
&(4)\ 4y - 5x = 0
\end{aligned}
$$

Equation of a Line. Suppose that we wish to find the equation which will describe the line in Figure 5. Because

the line is straight, this equation will be of the general form
$y = mx + k$. Here x and y are *variables*, pairs of numbers
either one of which may take on any value, while m and k

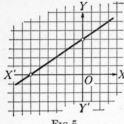

are *particular numbers*, still unknown, whose values depend upon
the law which connects x and y.
That law is implicit in the graph,
but when we discover the numerical
values of m and k, we can also express the relation in the form of an
equation.

Fig 5

By examining the graph we see
that it crosses the vertical axis at the point $(0, 4)$, and we
know that k must be 4.

We will select any two convenient points whose coördinates
seem easy to read, and will find the slope of the line as in
15 on page 100. Thus we see that $m = \frac{2}{3}$.

The equation of the line is therefore $y = \frac{2}{3}x + 4$, or
$3y = 2x + 12$.

As a check we will find one or two other pairs of numbers
which satisfy this equation, such as $(-6, 0)$, $(3, 6)$, $(-3, 2)$,
or $(-9, -2)$ and will verify the fact that the points which
have these number pairs for coördinates lie on the original
line.

An alternate method of solution is to select any two points
on the given line, such for example as $(3, 6)$ and $(-9, -2)$
and substitute their coördinates in the equation $y = mx + k$.

This would give us $\qquad 6 = 3m + k$

and $\qquad -2 = -9m + k$.

If we subtract the second of these equations from the first,
k will disappear, and we will have $8 = 12m$, from which we
see that $m = \frac{2}{3}$. Substituting $\frac{2}{3}$ for m in either of the equations,
gives us $k = 4$, as before.

EXERCISE 21

1. Find the equation for a line passing through the points (3, 4) and (5, 7).

2. Find the equation for each line in Figure 6.

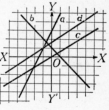

FIG. 6

SECOND TEST

1. Below is a list of equations and a list of phrases. Select all of the equations which are correctly described by the first phrase. Write the numbers of *all* such equations on the line at the right of this phrase. Do the same for each of the other phrases in the list.

a. An equation whose graph would pass through the origin. _____

b. An equation whose graph is not a straight line. _____

c. An equation whose graph is a straight line parallel to the graph of $x+4y=5$. _____

d. An equation whose graph is a straight line passing through the origin and lying wholly in the second and fourth quadrants. _____

e. An equation whose graph cuts the y-axis 2 units below the origin. _____

f. An equation whose graph is a straight line parallel to the y-axis. _____

g. An equation whose graph is a straight line passing through the origin and lying nearer to the y-axis than to the x-axis. _____

(1) $y=2x^2+3x-5$

(2) $y=5x-2$

(3) $x=7$

(4) $y=x^2-2x$

(5) $x=\frac{1}{5}y$

(6) $x+4y=0$

(7) $y=7x^2-2$

(8) $xy=24$

(9) $x+4y=-2$

(10) $x+y=0$

(11) $8y=5-2x$

2. Make a graph of the straight line which passes through the points $(1, -1)$ and $(4, 1)$ and find its equation.

3. Write the equation of the line which

(1) Crosses the y-axis 3 points below the origin and has a slope of $+4$.

(2) Crosses the y-axis at the origin and has a slope of $-\frac{3}{7}$.

4. On the same set of axes, make graphs of the equations $\begin{Bmatrix} 5x+4y=29 \\ 4x+3y=23 \end{Bmatrix}$ and find the coördinates of the point at which they intersect.

RADICALS

Initial Test

1. Multiply $\sqrt{\dfrac{2}{3}}$ by 3.

2. Multiply $\sqrt{\dfrac{a}{n} - \dfrac{b}{n^2}}$ by $\sqrt{n}$.

3. Multiply $\left[\dfrac{x^2}{N} - \left(\dfrac{a}{N}\right)^2\right]^{\frac{1}{2}}$ by N.

4. Divide $\sqrt{\dfrac{c}{x} - c^2}$ by c.

5. Substitute $\sigma_x = \dfrac{\sigma_1}{\sqrt{2(N_1 - 1)}}$ and $\sigma_y = \dfrac{\sigma_2}{\sqrt{2(N_2 - 1)}}$ in the formula

$$\sigma_{x-y} = (\sigma_x^2 + \sigma_y^2)^{\frac{1}{2}}.$$

6. Multiply both terms of the fraction $\dfrac{\dfrac{a}{x} - \dfrac{bc}{x^2}}{\sqrt{\dfrac{d}{x} - \dfrac{b^2}{x^2}} \sqrt{\dfrac{f}{x} - \dfrac{c^2}{x^2}}}$ by x^2.

7. Reduce $\sqrt{\dfrac{231}{75} - \left(\dfrac{8}{15}\right)^2}$ to a form in which the radicand is a single integer.

Importance. Most of the important statistical formulas encountered in an elementary course contain radicals. The student who cannot manipulate radicals easily is unable to take advantage of short cuts in computation and is usually bewildered by what seems to be a multiplicity of formulas for the same thing.

Terminology. The expression under a radical sign is called the *radicand*. The number 3 in $\sqrt[3]{a}$ is called the *index of the root.* In general $\sqrt[n]{a}$ is a root of the *n*th order. Two radicals are of the same order when they have the same index as $\sqrt[5]{xy}$ and $\sqrt[5]{3}$. Elementary work in statistics calls for continual use of square roots, but does not often make use of roots of higher order. It is customary to omit the index in writing square root, and conversely, when the index is not shown it is understood to be 2. Such numbers as 3, $17\frac{1}{2}$, $\frac{41}{68}$, and 3.29 are called *rational numbers.* The 3 is an integer and each of the others is the ratio of two integers, for $17\frac{1}{2}$ is $\frac{35}{2}$ or the ratio of 35 to 2, and 3.29 is $\frac{329}{100}$ or the ratio of 329 to 100. Such numbers as $\sqrt{17}$, $\sqrt[3]{4}$, $\sqrt[4]{8}$ are *irrational numbers* because they cannot be expressed as the *ratios* of integers. However, $\sqrt{16}$ is a rational number because it is equal to 4, and $\sqrt{\frac{4}{9}}$ is a rational number because it is equal to $\frac{2}{3}$.

It is awkward to write and especially awkward to print a radical when the radicand is a long complicated expression. For compactness and ease of writing, therefore, it is customary to indicate the square root of an algebraic expression by inclosing that expression in parentheses and using $\frac{1}{2}$ as an exponent. Thus $\sqrt{a-b}$ may be written as $(a-b)^{\frac{1}{2}}$, and whatever is said in the following paragraphs applies to one manner of writing the square root as well as to the other.

Multiplication and Division of Two Radicals.[1] To multiply two radicals of the same order, multiply their radicands. To divide one radical by another radical of the same order, divide the radicand of the first by the radicand of the second. The first group of examples below should make these rules seem reasonable, the second group should illustrate their utility.

Examples A.   (1) $\sqrt{36}\ \sqrt{25}$ $=\sqrt{900}=30$
                    Also $\sqrt{36}\ \sqrt{25}$ $=(6)(5)=30$

---

[1] It should be noted that we are considering only positive radicands.

$$(2) \qquad \sqrt{400} \div \sqrt{16} = \sqrt{25} = 5$$
$$\text{Also } \sqrt{400} \div \sqrt{16} = 20 \div 4 = 5$$

$$(3) \qquad \sqrt{\tfrac{1}{4}} \sqrt{36} \quad = \sqrt{9} \quad = 3$$
$$\text{Also } \sqrt{\tfrac{1}{4}} \sqrt{36} \quad = \tfrac{1}{2}(6) \quad = 3$$

Examples B.
$$(4) \qquad \sqrt{8} \sqrt{2} \quad = \sqrt{16} \quad = 4$$
$$(5) \qquad \sqrt{12} \div \sqrt{3} = \sqrt{4} \quad = 2$$

$$(6) \qquad \left(\frac{a}{x} - \frac{b^2}{x^2}\right)^{\frac{1}{2}} x^{\frac{1}{2}} \quad = \left(a - \frac{b^2}{x}\right)^{\frac{1}{2}}$$

$$(7) \qquad (a - bc)^{\frac{1}{2}} \div b^{\frac{1}{2}} \quad = \left(\frac{a}{b} - c\right)^{\frac{1}{2}}$$

Multiplication and Division of a Radical by Any Number.
To multiply a radical of the second order by any number,
multiply the radicand by the *square* of the number. To divide
a radical of the second order by any number, divide the radicand by the *square* of the number. Thus to multiply $\sqrt{15}$
by 2 we have

$$2 = \sqrt{4} \text{ and } 2\sqrt{15} = \sqrt{4} \sqrt{15} = \sqrt{60}.$$

To divide $\sqrt{243}$ by 3, we have

$$3 = \sqrt{9} \text{ and } \sqrt{243} \div \sqrt{9} = \sqrt{27}.$$

Taking Out a Rational Factor.   Computation with radicals
is often greatly facilitated by factoring the radicand into
two factors one of which is rational. The root of this rational
factor may then be extracted and the result multiplied by the
indicated root of the irrational factor.

Examples. (1) $\sqrt{640} = \sqrt{64} \sqrt{10} = 8\sqrt{10}$

$$(2) \quad \sqrt{\frac{27}{16}} = \sqrt{\frac{9}{16}} \sqrt{3} = \frac{3}{4}\sqrt{3}$$

This device provides a short cut for extracting certain roots.
It is easy to memorize the fact that $\sqrt{2} = 1.414$; $\sqrt{3} = 1.732$,

and $\sqrt{5}=2.236$. A quick method for finding such values as $\sqrt{8}$ or $\sqrt{75}$ is as follows:

$$\sqrt{8} \;=2\sqrt{2}=2(1.414)=2.828$$
$$\sqrt{75}=5\sqrt{3}=5(1.732)=8.660$$

Rationalizing a Denominator. It is obviously easier to find the approximate value of an irrational number which calls for multiplication by a radical, as $7\sqrt{5}$ or $\frac{2}{3}\sqrt{106}$, than of one which calls for division by a radical, as $\dfrac{7}{\sqrt{5}}$ or $\dfrac{2}{3\sqrt{106}}$. However, when both terms of the fraction $\dfrac{7}{\sqrt{5}}$ are multiplied by $\sqrt{5}$, we have $\dfrac{7\sqrt{5}}{5}$ with the radical in the numerator where it is easier to work with, arithmetically. This process is called *rationalizing the denominator*.

Examples. (1) $\sqrt{\dfrac{4}{27}}=\sqrt{\dfrac{12}{81}}=\sqrt{\dfrac{4}{81}}\sqrt{3}=\dfrac{2}{9}\sqrt{3}$

(2) $\sqrt{\dfrac{35}{120}-\left(\dfrac{7}{60}\right)^2}=\sqrt{\dfrac{1050}{3600}-\dfrac{49}{3600}}=\dfrac{1}{60}\sqrt{1001}$

Solution of Equations Involving Radicals. When an equation involves a single radical, the terms may be transposed so that the radical is in one member and all the remaining terms in the other. Then both members of the equation may be raised to a power corresponding to the index of the radical. This will remove the radical sign and the resulting equation can be readily solved.

Example. Solve $p-2\sqrt{\dfrac{pq}{n}}=0.60$ for n.

$$p-0.60 \;=2\sqrt{\dfrac{pq}{n}}$$

$$(p-0.60)^2 = \frac{4pq}{n}$$

$$n = \frac{4pq}{(p-0.60)^2}$$

Manipulation of a Statistical Formula. One formula for the Pearson correlation coefficient is

$$r = \frac{\Sigma x'y' - Nc_xc_y}{\sqrt{\Sigma(x')^2 - Nc_x^2}\,\sqrt{\Sigma(y')^2 - Nc_y^2}}.$$

There are many variant forms, all algebraically equivalent but looking very different to the person who cannot manipulate radicals. We must understand that $\Sigma x'y'$, $\Sigma(x')^2$ and $\Sigma(y')^2$ are each to be considered as representing a single integer. Suppose we divide both numerator and denominator of the fraction by N. In the denominator we will divide each factor by $\sqrt{N}$ so that the product may be divided by $\sqrt{N} \cdot \sqrt{N} = N$. The resultant formula is

$$r = \frac{\dfrac{\Sigma x'y'}{N} - c_xc_y}{\sqrt{\dfrac{\Sigma(x')^2}{N} - c_x^2}\,\sqrt{\dfrac{\Sigma(y')^2}{N} - c_y^2}}.$$

EXERCISE 22

1. Given $\sqrt{2} = 1.41$ $\sqrt{6} = 2.45$
$\sqrt{3} = 1.73$ $\sqrt{7} = 2.65$
$\sqrt{5} = 2.24$ $\sqrt{10} = 3.16$

Without extracting any roots or using any tables or helps except the six values listed above, find the values of the square root of each of the following:

    (1) 20   (4) 75
    (2) $\frac{2}{3}$ (5) $\frac{1}{8}$
    (3) $\frac{5}{18}$ (6) $\frac{6}{8}$

2. (1) If the denominator of the fraction in $\sqrt{\dfrac{3}{5}}$ is multiplied by 4, the result is ——— and this value is (just as large, twice as large, four times as large, half as large, one-fourth as large) as the original expression.

(2) If the numerator of the fraction in $\sqrt{\dfrac{3}{5}}$ is multiplied by 4, the result is ——— and this value is (just as large, twice as large, four times as large, half as large, one-fourth as large) as the original expression.

(3) If both terms of the fraction in $\sqrt{\dfrac{3}{5}}$ are multiplied by 4, the result is ——— and this value is (just as large, twice as large, four times as large, half as large, one-fourth as large) as the original expression.

(4) To multiply $\sqrt{\dfrac{2}{5}}$ by 3, we should multiply the numerator of the fraction by ———.

(5) To divide $\sqrt{400}$ by 4 we should divide the radicand (i.e., 400) by ———.

3. From the four answers given, select the correct one and write its number on the blank line at the right.

		1	*2*	*3*	*4*	
(1)	$2\sqrt{6}$	$= 12$	$\sqrt{6}$	$\sqrt{12}$	$\sqrt{24}$	———
(2)	$2\sqrt{\dfrac{1}{3}}$	$= \dfrac{2}{3}$	$\sqrt{\dfrac{2}{3}}$	$\sqrt{\dfrac{4}{3}}$	$\sqrt{\dfrac{1}{6}}$	———
(3)	$\dfrac{1}{2}\sqrt{5}$	$= \dfrac{5}{2}$	$\sqrt{\dfrac{5}{2}}$	$\sqrt{\dfrac{5}{4}}$	$\sqrt{10}$	———
(4)	$\dfrac{1}{3}\sqrt{\dfrac{2}{5}}$	$= \dfrac{2}{15}$	$\sqrt{\dfrac{2}{15}}$	$\sqrt{\dfrac{6}{15}}$	$\sqrt{\dfrac{2}{45}}$	———
(5)	$\sqrt{\dfrac{1}{3}}\sqrt{\dfrac{2}{5}}$	$= \dfrac{2}{15}$	$\sqrt{\dfrac{2}{15}}$	$\sqrt{\dfrac{2}{45}}$	$\sqrt{\dfrac{6}{15}}$	———
(6)	$N\sqrt{\dfrac{a}{b}}$	$= \dfrac{Na}{b}$	$\sqrt{\dfrac{aN^2}{b}}$	$\sqrt{\dfrac{aN}{b}}$	$\sqrt{\dfrac{aN}{bN}}$	———

		1	*2*	*3*	*4*
(7)	$\sqrt{\dfrac{a}{b}}\sqrt{\dfrac{a}{b}} =$	$\dfrac{a}{b}$	$\sqrt{\dfrac{a}{b}}$	1	$\dfrac{a^2}{b^2}$
(8)	$\sqrt{\dfrac{a}{b}}\sqrt{\dfrac{b}{a}} =$	$\dfrac{a}{b}$	$\sqrt{\dfrac{a}{b}}$	1	$\dfrac{a^2}{b^2}$

4. From the three answers given, select the correct one and write its number on the blank line at the right.

		1	*2*	*3*	
(1)	$a\sqrt{\dfrac{b}{c}-d}$	$=\sqrt{\dfrac{ab}{c}-d}$	$\sqrt{\dfrac{a^2b}{c}-a^2d}$	$\sqrt{\dfrac{ab}{c}-ad}$	
(2)	$a\sqrt{\dfrac{b}{a}-\dfrac{c^2}{a^2}}$	$=\sqrt{b-c^2}$	$\sqrt{ab-c^2}$	$\sqrt{b-\dfrac{c^2}{a}}$	
(3)	$N\sqrt{\dfrac{a}{N}-\left(\dfrac{b}{N}\right)^2}$	$=\sqrt{aN-b^2}$	$\sqrt{a-b^2}$	$\sqrt{a-\dfrac{b^2}{N}}$	
(4)	$\dfrac{1}{N}\left(a-\dfrac{bc}{N}\right)$	$=\dfrac{a}{N}-\dfrac{bc}{N^2}$	$\dfrac{a-bc}{N^2}$	$\dfrac{aN-bc}{N}$	
(5)	$N^2\left(\dfrac{a}{N}-\dfrac{bc}{N^2}\right)$	$=\dfrac{Na-bc}{N^2}$	$Na-bc$	$Na-\dfrac{bc}{N^2}$	
(6)	$\dfrac{1}{x}\sqrt{\dfrac{x}{a}-\dfrac{x}{b}}$	$=\sqrt{\dfrac{1}{a}-\dfrac{1}{b}}$	$\sqrt{\dfrac{1}{ax}-\dfrac{1}{bx}}$	$\sqrt{\dfrac{x}{a-b}}$	

5. Reduce each of the following to a form in which the radicand is a single integer, and the whole radical is multiplied by a fraction, as $\frac{2}{7}\sqrt{97}$ or $\frac{1}{16}(419)^{\frac{1}{2}}$.

(1) $\sqrt{\frac{3}{4}-\frac{5}{16}}$

(2) $\sqrt{\frac{23}{25}-\left(\frac{3}{25}\right)^2}$

(3) $\sqrt{\frac{59}{8}-\left(\frac{15}{8}\right)^2}$

(4) $\left\{\frac{510}{80}-\left(\frac{-3}{20}\right)^2\right\}^{\frac{1}{2}}$

(5) $\left\{\frac{35}{6}+\frac{7}{3}-\left(\frac{2}{3}\right)^2\right\}^{\frac{1}{2}}$

(6) $\left\{\frac{175}{32}-\left(\frac{-11}{8}\right)^2\right\}^{\frac{1}{2}}$

6. If $r_{1.23}=[1-(1-r_{12}^2)(1-r_{13.2}^2)]^{\frac{1}{2}}$ find $r_{1.23}$ when

(1) $r_{12}=-.80$ and $r_{13.2}=-.40$

(2) $r_{12}=1.00$ and $r_{13.2}=.70$

(3) $r_{12}=0.10$ and $r_{13.2}=0.0$

7. Multiply

(1) $\sqrt{\dfrac{a}{b}}$ by b

(2) $\sqrt{\dfrac{ax}{n}}$ by $\sqrt{x}$

(3) $\sqrt{\dfrac{ax}{n}}$ by $\sqrt{n}$

(4) $\sqrt{\dfrac{1}{c}-a}$ by $\sqrt{c}$

(5) $\sqrt{\dfrac{1}{c}-a}$ by c

(6) $\left\{\dfrac{a}{b}-c\right\}^{\frac{1}{2}}$ by b

(7) $\left\{\dfrac{a}{n}-\left(\dfrac{b}{n}\right)^2\right\}^{\frac{1}{2}}$ by $n^{\frac{1}{2}}$

(8) $\sqrt{\dfrac{x}{c}}$ by $\sqrt{\dfrac{c}{d}}$

(9) $\sqrt{\dfrac{3}{4}}$ by 2

(10) $\sqrt{\dfrac{3}{8}}$ by 4

8. Multiply $\dfrac{r_{12}-r_{13}r_{23}}{\sqrt{1-r_{13}^2}\sqrt{1-r_{23}^2}}$ by $\dfrac{\sqrt{1-r_{13}^2}}{\sqrt{1-r_{23}^2}}$.

9. If $\sigma_{x-y}=\sqrt{\sigma_x^2+\sigma_y^2}$, write the formula for σ_{x-y} when

(1) $\sigma_x=\sqrt{\dfrac{p_1q_1}{n_1}}$ and $\sigma_y=\sqrt{\dfrac{p_2q_2}{n_2}}$

(2) $\sigma_x=\dfrac{1-r_1^2}{\sqrt{N}}$ and $\sigma_y=\dfrac{1-r_2^2}{\sqrt{N}}$

10. Multiply $\sqrt{\dfrac{t}{q}-\left(\dfrac{r}{q}\right)^2}$ by q.

11. Multiply the same expression by $\sqrt{q}$.

12. Multiply both terms of the fraction $\dfrac{\dfrac{p}{q}-\dfrac{rs}{q^2}}{\sqrt{\dfrac{t}{q}-\left(\dfrac{r}{q}\right)^2}\sqrt{\dfrac{u}{q}-\left(\dfrac{s}{q}\right)^2}}$

by q^2.

13. Multiply both terms of that fraction by q.

14. Multiply $\sqrt{\dfrac{\Sigma(x')^2}{N}-\left(\dfrac{\Sigma x'}{N}\right)^2}$ by N, treating $\Sigma(x')^2$ as a single number and $\Sigma x'$ as another single number. You do not need to understand the meaning of either expression, but merely manipulate them as numbers.

15. Multiply both terms of the fraction

$$\frac{\frac{\Sigma XY}{N}-\left(\frac{\Sigma X}{N}\right)\left(\frac{\Sigma Y}{N}\right)}{\sqrt{\frac{\Sigma X^2}{N}-\left(\frac{\Sigma X}{N}\right)^2}\sqrt{\frac{\Sigma Y^2}{N}-\left(\frac{\Sigma Y}{N}\right)^2}}$$

by N, treating ΣXY, ΣX, ΣX^2, ΣY, and ΣY^2 each as a single number. This formula for the correlation coefficient is one of the very common statistical formulas. While the answer can be written in various forms, the one given in the answer key is a form commonly found in statistics texts.

16. Multiply both terms of the same fraction by N^2.

17. $S=\dfrac{a}{\sqrt{2N}}.$

(1) Find S if $a=3.2$ and $N=75$.
(2) If a is doubled but N remains the same, what will be the value of S?
(3) If a is unchanged but N is doubled, what will be the value of S?
(4) What is the general effect on S of increasing a? Of increasing N?

18. Solve $\sigma_{x-y}=\sqrt{\sigma_x^2-2r\sigma_x\sigma_y+\sigma_y^2}$ for r.

19. If $S=\dfrac{1-r^2}{\sqrt{N}}$, find S when

(1) $r=.62,\ N=175$
(2) $r=.93,\ N=523$

20. If $r_1=\dfrac{r_2-r_3r_4}{\sqrt{1-r_3^2}\ \sqrt{1-r_4^2}}$, find r_1 when

(1) $r_2=.85,\ r_3=.20,\ r_4=.60$
(2) $r_2=.72,\ r_3=-.12,\ r_4=.35$

21. Solve $p-3\sqrt{\dfrac{pq}{n}}=0.50$ for n.

Second Test

1. Multiply $\sqrt{\frac{3}{5}}$ by 5.

2. Multiply $\sqrt{\dfrac{c}{r} - \dfrac{x}{r^2}}$ by r.

3. Multiply $\left\{ \dfrac{\Sigma X^2}{N} - M^2 \right\}^{\frac{1}{2}}$ by $N^{\frac{1}{2}}$.

4. Divide $\sqrt{x^2 - \dfrac{x}{a}}$ by x.

5. Substitute $\sigma_x = \dfrac{\sigma_1}{\sqrt{N}}$ and $\sigma_y = \dfrac{\sigma_2}{\sqrt{N}}$ in the formula

$$\sigma_{x-y} = \{ \sigma_x^2 - 2r\sigma_x\sigma_y + \sigma_y^2 \}^{\frac{1}{2}}$$

6. Divide both terms of the fraction $\dfrac{a - \dfrac{bc}{d}}{\sqrt{x - \dfrac{b^2}{d}} \sqrt{y - \dfrac{c^2}{d}}}$ by d.

7. Reduce $\sqrt{\dfrac{107}{24} - \left(\dfrac{5}{12}\right)^2}$ to a form in which the radicand is a single integer.

XIII

SYMBOLISM IN STATISTICS

Lack of Uniformity. Because statistical theory is a new science, its language is still developing, and writers vary somewhat among themselves in regard to certain details, as if they spoke slightly different dialects of the same mother tongue. The student who uses symbolism creatively, who can express his own ideas in symbolic language, will soon learn to pass easily from the symbols used by one writer to those used by another, since a common principle underlies them all. The student who memorizes symbolism without making it a living language will always be greatly disturbed and perhaps completely balked by slight changes from the symbolism to which he is accustomed.

Definitions. Suppose that a group of 10 children have been given a test with scores as follows: 17, 16, 16, 15, 15, 15, 14, 14, 13, 12. The mean score is found by adding the ten individual scores and dividing by 10.

Let X = a score,
and M_x = arithmetic mean of the scores,
and N = number of cases.

Then $M_x = \dfrac{\Sigma X}{N}$. This is the definition of the arithmetic mean.

The subscript may be either a capital or a small letter, its purpose being merely to indicate which of several means is referred to.

Σ is the Greek letter sigma corresponding to our capital S, and means "the sum of "

In this case $\Sigma X = 147$, and $M_x = \dfrac{147}{10} = 14.7$.

Now let x be the deviation of a score from the mean score; that is, x is the difference found by subtracting the mean from the score of an individual. $x = X - M_x$.

For the ten scores, we then have

$X_1 = 17$	$x_1 = 17 - 14.7 = 2.3$
$X_2 = 16$	$x_2 = 16 - 14.7 = 1.3$
$X_3 = 16$	$x_3 = 16 - 14.7 = 1.3$
$X_4 = 15$	$x_4 = 15 - 14.7 = .3$
$X_5 = 15$	$x_5 = 15 - 14.7 = .3$
$X_6 = 15$	$x_6 = 15 - 14.7 = .3$
$X_7 = 14$	$x_7 = 14 - 14.7 = -.7$
$X_8 = 14$	$x_8 = 14 - 14.7 = -.7$
$X_9 = 13$	$x_9 = 13 - 14.7 = -1.7$
$X_{10} = 12$	$x_{10} = 12 - 14.7 = -2.7$

Add to find the value of Σx. It is a characteristic of the arithmetic mean that the positive and negative deviations (or differences) from it balance each other, so that Σx is always 0.

Now let M_x' be some value which we will guess to be the mean and from which we will compute deviations. If the sum (algebraic sum) of the deviations from M_x' does not equal zero, we will know that our guess was in error, and we will correct it by an amount which will make the sum of the deviations zero.

Let x' be a deviation from the guessed mean so that $x' = X - M_x'$, and let $c_x = M_x - M_x'$. When there is no need to distinguish c_x, c_y, c_z, etc., the subscript can be safely omitted, and we may write merely $c = M - M'$. Notice that a prime is used when we are dealing with an assumed mean. The distinction between M and M' is that the first is the mean of the distribution while the second is only an assumed mean, a guessed average, an arbitrary reference point used for the sake of simplifying computation. The distinction between x and x' is that x is a deviation from the true mean and x' is a deviation from the assumed mean. Then c is the amount we must add to M' to get M. For illustration, suppose we had guessed the mean of the ten scores to be 15. $M'=15$.

For the ten scores we now have:

$$
\begin{aligned}
x_1' &= 17-15 = 2 \\
x_2' &= 16-15 = 1 \\
x_3' &= 16-15 = 1 \\
x_4' &= 15-15 = 0 \\
x_5' &= 15-15 = 0 \\
x_6' &= 15-15 = 0 \\
x_7' &= 14-15 = -1 \\
x_8' &= 14-15 = -1 \\
x_9' &= 13-15 = -2 \\
x_{10}' &= 12-15 = -3
\end{aligned}
$$

Here we have

$$\Sigma x' = 4-7 = -3$$

$$c = \frac{\Sigma x'}{N} = -0.3$$

and $M = M'+c = 15-0.3 = 14.7$, which is the value we found by the formula $M = \dfrac{\Sigma X}{N}$.

EXERCISE 23

1. What is the value of $x_1'-x_1$? $x_2'-x_2$? $x_7'-x_7$? $x_{10}'-x_{10}$?
2. Write a formula connecting x, x', and c_x.

The Standard Deviation. The mean will serve to measure the central tendency of these scores, but it gives no idea of how much they scatter. To measure the scattering of the scores away from the mean, or their tendency to cluster around it we need some sort of an average of the deviations from the mean. But if we average them in the usual way, adding deviations and dividing by 10, we find merely that $\dfrac{\Sigma x}{N} = \dfrac{0}{10} = 0$. This sum will always be zero, because the positive and negative deviations balance each other. Consequently we need to get rid of the negative signs, and this can be done by squaring the deviations. Then we have

$$
\begin{aligned}
x_1^2 &= (2.3)^2 = 5.29 \\
x_2^2 &= (1.3)^2 = 1.69 \\
x_3^2 &= (1.3)^2 = 1.69 \\
x_4^2 &= (.3)^2 = .09 \\
x_5^2 &= (.3)^2 = .09 \\
x_6^2 &= (.3)^2 = .09 \\
x_7^2 &= (-.7)^2 = .49 \\
x_8^2 &= (-.7)^2 = .49 \\
x_9^2 &= (-1.7)^2 = 2.89 \\
x_{10}^2 &= (-2.7)^2 = 7.29 \\
\hline
\Sigma x^2 &= 20.10
\end{aligned}
$$

If we divide this sum by 10, we have 2.01 which is an average of the squared deviations, a *mean square deviation*, often called the *variance*. Now we will take the square root of this mean square deviation in order to undo the effect of the squaring, so far as that is possible. The result is called the *root mean square deviation*, or more often the *standard deviation*, and is designated by the small Greek sigma, σ.

Here $\sigma = \sqrt{2.01} = 1.42$

In order to write a formula for σ, let us examine this process step by step.

First, we squared the deviations from the mean. $\qquad x^2$

Then we added all such squares. $\qquad \Sigma x^2$

Then we divided this sum by the number of cases, which gave us the mean of the squared deviations. $\qquad \dfrac{\Sigma x^2}{N}$

Then we took the square root of the result. $\qquad \sqrt{\dfrac{\Sigma x^2}{N}}$

Accordingly, the formula for the standard deviation is $\qquad \sigma = \sqrt{\dfrac{\Sigma x^2}{N}}$

Computing the Standard Deviation from an Assumed Mean. The two questions in Exercise 23 have shown us that $x_1' = x_1 + c$. Translate this equation into words. How many such equations are there? If we square both sides of this equation we have $(x_1')^2 = x_1^2 + 2x_1c + c^2$. For the ten scores we have been considering there are ten equations like this. These are:

$$(x_1')^2 = x_1^2 + 2x_1c + c^2 \text{ or } (\ \ \ 2.3)^2 + 2(2.3)(-.3) \ \ \ + (-.3)^2$$
$$(x_2')^2 = x_2^2 + 2x_2c + c^2 \text{ or } (\ \ \ 1.3)^2 + 2(1.3)(-.3) \ \ \ + (-.3)^2$$
$$(x_3')^2 = x_3^2 + 2x_3c + c^2 \text{ or } (\ \ \ 1.3)^2 + 2(1.3)(-.3) \ \ \ + (-.3)^2$$
$$(x_4')^2 = x_4^2 + 2x_4c + c^2 \text{ or } (\ \ \ 0.3)^2 + 2(0.3)(-.3) \ \ \ + (-.3)^2$$
$$(x_5')^2 = x_5^2 + 2x_5c + c^2 \text{ or } (\ \ \ 0.3)^2 + 2(0.3)(-.3) \ \ \ + (-.3)^2$$
$$(x_6')^2 = x_6^2 + 2x_6c + c^2 \text{ or } (\ \ \ 0.3)^2 + 2(0.3)(-.3) \ \ \ + (-.3)^2$$
$$(x_7')^2 = x_7^2 + 2x_7c + c^2 \text{ or } (-0.7)^2 + 2(-0.7)(-.3) + (-.3)^2$$
$$(x_8')^2 = x_8^2 + 2x_8c + c^2 \text{ or } (-0.7)^2 + 2(-0.7)(-.3) + (-.3)^2$$
$$(x_9')^2 = x_9^2 + 2x_9c + c^2 \text{ or } (-1.7)^2 + 2(-1.7)(-.3) + (-.3)^2$$
$$(x_{10}')^2 = x_{10}^2 + 2x_{10}c + c^2 \text{ or } (-2.7)^2 + 2(-2.7)(-.3) + (-.3)^2$$

Adding:

$$\Sigma(x')^2 = \Sigma x^2 + \Sigma 2xc + \Sigma c^2 \text{ or } 20.1 \ + \ \ \ \ \ \ \ 0 \ \ \ \ \ + \ \ 0.9$$

Notice that all the values of c^2 are exactly alike, so their sum is $10c^2$, whereas the values of $(x')^2$ differ from one individual to the next, so that their sum must be written $\Sigma(x')^2$. The middle term in the right hand number, $\Sigma 2xc$, is really

$$2x_1c + 2x_2c + \cdots + 2x_{10}c = 2c(x_1 + x_2 + \cdots + x_{10})$$
$$= 2c\Sigma x.$$

This can be seen clearly from the numerical substitution above. We have already seen that $\Sigma x = 0$. Therefore the middle term is zero, and we have

$$\Sigma(x')^2 = \Sigma x^2 + 10c^2.$$

Dividing both sides by 10,

$$\frac{\Sigma(x')^2}{10} = \frac{\Sigma x^2}{10} + c^2$$

or, in general

$$\frac{\Sigma(x')^2}{N} = \frac{\Sigma x^2}{N} + c^2.$$

Solving for $\frac{\Sigma x^2}{N}$, we have $\frac{\Sigma x^2}{N} = \frac{\Sigma(x')^2}{N} - c^2.$

Taking the square root of both sides of the equation,

$$\sqrt{\frac{\Sigma x^2}{N}} = \sqrt{\frac{\Sigma(x')^2}{N} - c^2}.$$

Therefore we may compute σ by the formula $\sigma = \sqrt{\frac{\Sigma(x')^2}{N} - c^2}$,

which is easier to use in computing than the form $\sigma = \sqrt{\frac{\Sigma x^2}{N}}$

because deviations from the mean usually are fractions difficult to square.

Going back now to the numerical values for the x's we have:

$$
\begin{aligned}
(x_1')^2 = &\quad 2^2 = 4 \\
(x_2')^2 = &\quad 1^2 = 1 \\
(x_3')^2 = &\quad 1^2 = 1 \\
(x_4')^2 = &\quad 0^2 = 0 \\
(x_5')^2 = &\quad 0^2 = 0 \\
(x_6')^2 = &\quad 0^2 = 0 \\
(x_7')^2 = &(-1)^2 = 1 \\
(x_8')^2 = &(-1)^2 = 1 \\
(x_9')^2 = &(-2)^2 = 4 \\
(x_{10}')^2 = &(-3)^2 = \underline{9} \\
& \qquad\qquad 21
\end{aligned}
$$

Then $\Sigma(x')^2 = 21$.

$$\sqrt{\frac{\Sigma(x')^2}{N} - c_x^2} = \sqrt{\frac{21}{10} - (-.3)^2} = \sqrt{2.01} = 1.42.$$

This is the same result as we obtained by the formula

$$\sigma = \sqrt{\frac{\Sigma x^2}{N}}.$$

Computation with Grouped Frequencies. In the list of ten scores used in the foregoing illustrations we had two scores of 16, three of 15, and two of 14. The distribution might then have been written as follows.

X	f
17	1
16	2
15	3
14	2
13	1
12	1

To compute the mean from this distribution, we must not fail to remember that the score 15 is to be used three times, so that the corresponding value of x' or $(x')^2$ is to be multiplied by 3. Three is the *class frequency* of the score 15. The computations from this grouped distribution would be as follows:

X	f	x'	fx'	$f(x')^2$
17	1	2	2	4
16	2	1	2	2
15	3	0	0	0
14	2	−1	−2	2
13	1	−2	−2	4
12	1	−3	−3	9
	10		−7	21
			+4	
			−3	

It now seems appropriate to introduce an f (f=frequency) into the formulas, writing

$$\Sigma fx' = -3, \quad \Sigma f(x')^2 = 21, \quad N = \Sigma f,$$

$$\sigma = \sqrt{\frac{\Sigma fx^2}{N}} = \sqrt{\frac{\Sigma f(x')^2}{N} - c_x^2} = \sqrt{\frac{21}{10} - (-.3)^2}.$$

Study this computation until you understand that the only difference between it and the work on page 120 is in the form in which it is set down. The chief reason for writing f into the formulas is to warn the novice not to overlook f in his computation. The f is a sort of flag waving to warn the absent minded not to overlook the class frequencies.

Computations with a Step Interval Other than One.
Sometimes our measurements are such that it is more convenient to use a step interval which is either larger than 1 or smaller than 1. For example, suppose that the heights of 20 children of the same age are found to be, in inches, $30\frac{1}{2}$, 30, 30, $29\frac{1}{2}$, $29\frac{1}{2}$, $29\frac{1}{2}$, 29, $28\frac{1}{2}$, $28\frac{1}{2}$, 28, 28, 28, $27\frac{1}{2}$, $27\frac{1}{2}$, 27, 27, 27, 26, 26, $25\frac{1}{2}$. The computation of the mean and standard deviation might be arranged as follows:

x	f	x'	fx'	$f(x')^2$
$30\frac{1}{2}$	1	5	5	25
30	2	4	8	32
$29\frac{1}{2}$	3	3	9	27
29	1	2	2	4
$28\frac{1}{2}$	2	1	2	2
28	3	0	0	0
$27\frac{1}{2}$	2	−1	−2	2
27	3	−2	−6	12
$26\frac{1}{2}$	0	−3	0	0
26	2	−4	−8	32
$25\frac{1}{2}$	1	−5	−5	25
	20		5	161

Height was measured to the nearest half-inch. We have a step interval of one-half. The values in the columns headed x', fx', and $f(x')^2$ are in terms of half-inch step intervals, not inches. The children with height $29\frac{1}{2}$ are 3 step intervals above the mean, 3 half-inches. To compute the mean we add the correction, $c = \dfrac{\Sigma fx'}{N}$ to the assumed mean. But

$\frac{\Sigma fx'}{N} = \frac{5}{20}$ is in terms of step intervals while $M' = 28$ is in terms of inches, and these two values cannot be added until they are reduced to the same denomination. The correction must be multiplied by the width of the step interval to bring it to the same denomination as the assumed mean. Therefore $M = 28 + \frac{1}{4}(\frac{1}{2}) = 28\frac{1}{8}$.

In computing the standard deviation by the formula $\sigma = \sqrt{\frac{\Sigma f(x')^2}{N} - c^2}$ shall we use $c = \frac{1}{4}$, which is in terms of step intervals, or $c = \frac{1}{8}$, which is in terms of inches? The question can be answered by noting that $\frac{\Sigma f(x')^2}{N} = \frac{161}{20}$ is in terms of the step interval. Certainly any number subtracted from it must be expressed in step intervals also. Therefore

$$\sigma = \sqrt{\frac{161}{20} - \left(\frac{1}{4}\right)^2} = 2.8 \text{ (step intervals) or}$$

$$\sigma = \frac{1}{2}\sqrt{\frac{161}{20} - \left(\frac{1}{4}\right)^2} = 1.4 \text{ (inches)}.$$

If we let $i =$ width of step interval and $c =$ correction in terms of step intervals, then we have

$$M = M' + ci,$$

$$\sigma(\text{step intervals}) = \sqrt{\frac{\Sigma f(x')^2}{N} - c^2},$$

$$\sigma(\text{inches}) \qquad = i\sqrt{\frac{\Sigma f(x')^2}{N} - c^2}.$$

The whole matter of knowing when to multiply c by the step interval and when not to do so is very simple. It really involves nothing more than the familiar fact that when two numbers are to be combined they must be in the same denomination. We may describe a line as being either 18 in. long or 1½ ft. long, and we are not confused because two numerical measurements of the same thing look very unlike. If, however, a table is 18 in. by 3 ft., and we want an expression for the area of its top, we know we cannot say its area is 18×3. We cannot combine these two numbers until both are in the same denomination, either $18 \times 36 = 648$ or $1\frac{1}{2} \times 3 = 4\frac{1}{2}$. In the same way, c may be expressed either as a certain number of step intervals, or as a certain number of scores (inches, dollars, years, or whatever the scale unit may be), and the standard deviation may likewise be expressed in the same ways. It is only a matter of common sense to recognize that when one term in a formula is expressed in step interval units the terms which combine with it must be expressed in the same units. When one term is expressed in score units other terms which combine with it must be expressed in score units also.

EXERCISE 24

1. Below is a set of symbols and also a set of descriptive phrases. Look among the phrases until you find one which translates the first symbol, then write the number of this phrase on the line at the left of that symbol. Since there are more symbols than phrases, the same phrase may apply to more than one symbol. If more than one phrase properly describes the same symbol, write both numbers on the line at the left of that symbol.

————σ

————M_x

————x'

————X

————M_x'

————Σx

$\dfrac{(\Sigma f x')}{N}$

$\dfrac{\Sigma f X}{N}$

(1) A class frequency

(2) A mean

(3) An assumed mean

(4) The sum of all the class frequencies

(5) A standard deviation

(6) A deviation from the true mean

(7) A deviation from an assumed mean

(8) Zero

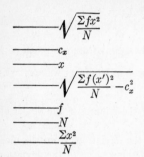

$$\underline{\hspace{2cm}}\sqrt{\frac{\Sigma f x^2}{N}}$$

$$\underline{\hspace{2cm}}c_x$$

$$\underline{\hspace{2cm}}x$$

$$\underline{\hspace{2cm}}\sqrt{\frac{\Sigma f (x')^2}{N} - c_x^2}$$

$$\underline{\hspace{2cm}}f$$

$$\underline{\hspace{2cm}}N$$

$$\underline{\hspace{2cm}}\frac{\Sigma x^2}{N}$$

(9) The amount which must be added to the assumed mean to produce the true mean

(10) The number of cases

(11) The mean of the squared deviations from the mean

(12) A score

(13) The variance

(14) The square root of the variance

2. Sometimes it is necessary to use different letters to distinguish between the scores on various tests. If you have mastered the general plan of the symbols used in this section, you will be able to apply it when a score is named Y or Z or something other than X. Suppose we have given a class four tests which we will call X, Y, Z, and W.

(1) Write a formula to represent the total score of pupil 7 on the sum of the four tests.

(2) Write a formula to represent the difference between the mean score of the class on test X and on test Y.

(3) If the four tests are given to an entire class, what is the relation between N_x, N_y, N_z, and N_w? Could the subscripts be omitted?

3. Translate these verbal statements into symbolic statements, using the letter Y instead of X to designate the trait.

(1) The sum of the deviations from the mean is zero.

(2) The mean can be found by adding the scores and dividing by the number of scores.

(3) The mean can be found by taking an assumed mean and adding to it the mean of the deviations from the assumed mean. Note that the symbol $\frac{\Sigma}{N}$ is a general pattern expressing a mean, so that $\frac{\Sigma y'}{N}$ is the mean of the deviations of

a set of scores in Y from an assumed mean, $\dfrac{\Sigma y^2}{N}$ is the mean of the squares of the deviations from the mean of Y, and $\dfrac{\Sigma (\quad)}{N}$ indicates the mean of whatever we may write in the parenthesis.

(4) The variance is the mean of the squares of the deviations from the mean.

(5) The mean of the squares of the deviations from the mean is less than ($<$) the mean of the squares of the deviations from any other reference point.

(6) The sum of the class frequencies is the number of cases in the distribution.

4. For the ten scores with which we have been computing throughout this section (see page 115), we found $M_x = 14.7$ and $\sigma_x = 1.42$. Now add 5 to each of the original scores, making the list 22, 21, 21, 20, 20, 20, 19, 19, 18, 17. Compute the mean and standard deviation for this new distribution.

5. Subtract 2 from each of these scores and compute the mean and standard deviation.

6. Formulate a general rule stating the effect upon a mean and the effect upon a standard deviation of adding a constant amount to all the scores.

7. Study the following, and translate each important statement into words. State the final conclusion in words. If we add a to each score, then a score will be $X + a$,

$$M_{x+a} = \frac{\Sigma(X+a)}{N} = \frac{\Sigma X}{N} + \frac{\Sigma a}{N} = \frac{\Sigma X}{N} + \frac{Na}{N} = \frac{\Sigma X}{N} + a.$$

Therefore $\qquad M_{x+a} = M_x + a.$

A deviation from the mean of the new series would be

$$(X+a) - M_{x+a} = X + a - (M_x + a) = X - M_x = x.$$

Then $\qquad \sigma_{x+a} = \sqrt{\dfrac{\Sigma x^2}{N}} = \sigma_x.$

8. An algebra test was given to 400 high school children, of whom 150 were boys and 250 were girls. The results were as follows:

$$N_B = 150 \qquad\qquad N_G = 250$$
$$M_B = 72.5 \qquad\qquad M_G = 73.6$$
$$\sigma_B = 7.0 \qquad\qquad \sigma_G = 6.4$$

After the means had been obtained for boys and girls separately, the mean for the combined groups was needed and was found by the formula

$$M_c = \frac{N_B M_B + N_G M_G}{N_c}.$$

(1) Put this formula into words.
(2) Write a formula for finding N_c from the data you have given.
(3) Find M_c.
(4) If $d_B = M_B - M_c$, find the numerical value of d_B. Translate this statement into words. (d = difference.)
(5) Write the formula for finding d_G and find its numerical value.
(6) Compute σ_c by the formula

$$N_c \sigma_c^2 = N_B(\sigma_B^2 + d_B^2) + N_G(\sigma_G^2 + d_G^2).$$

9. How many values of M may there be for a single distribution of scores? How many values of M'?

10. Suppose that zero is used as an assumed mean. Notice that the deviation of any score from this mean is just the score itself. What is the correction for the assumed mean? Show that in this case the formula for computing the standard deviation becomes

$$\sigma = \sqrt{\frac{\Sigma f X^2}{N} - M^2}.$$

PART TWO

XIV

VARIABLE, UNKNOWN, PARAMETER, FUNCTION

Importance. Students of statistics are often handicapped because they have never acquired a clear concept of variables. The texts in elementary algebra have sometimes contributed to this haziness of thinking by failing to distinguish between variables and unknowns. When these two are confused, clear thinking on statistical problems is hampered.

Constant. Certain symbols, such as the numbers 1, 2, 3, etc., always have the same meaning whenever they are used in a mathematical expression. There are also a few letters which have a constant meaning. For example the Greek letter π represents the ratio of a circle to its diameter. Its value is unchanging but cannot be expressed with complete numerical accuracy, such values as $\frac{22}{7}$, 3.14, 3.1416, and 3.14159 being approximations to the real value. Another number with important mathematical properties, whose numerical value like that of π can be stated only approximately, is denoted by the letter e. Its numerical value is approximately 2.71828. This e is the base of the system of natural logarithms and is of great importance in the relations studied in the calculus. In statistical theory it occurs in the formula for the curve of error, often called the "normal" curve. In the same way the letter g is used by a physicist to represent the acceleration in feet per second in the speed of a falling body due to gravity alone. It is approximately 32. These letters represent constants just as do such number symbols as 7, $2\sqrt{10}$, or $\frac{4}{5}$.

Unknown. An unknown is a number whose value is temporarily unknown, often represented in algebraic problems by the initial letter of a word or by x, y, or z. Thus in one problem v may stand for the velocity of a projectile in feet per second while in another problem v may stand for the volume of a solid in cubic centimeters. The initial letters of words are often used because of their suggestiveness. Sometimes however this practice leads to duplication and confusion, and therefore elementary algebra makes much use of the letters x and y to represent unknown numbers. A letter used in this way has the same value throughout one problem, represents a particular number or particular numbers in that problem, but is used in another problem for an entirely different number or numbers. Thus the equation $12+x=25$ asks the question "What number can be added to 12 to produce 25?" This question has only one answer, and x is representing the single number 13, temporarily unknown to us. The equation $3x^2+2x=16$ is asking the question, "What is the number such that the sum of twice the number and three times the square of the number will be 16?" This question has two answers, 2 and $-\frac{8}{3}$, but no more. Here x represents these two out of all possible numbers. If we had an equation involving x^3, there would be 3 values for x. In general if we have an equation in which x^n is the highest power of x, that equation has n roots, n values of x which satisfy the equation, and no more. The unknown number may have many values, but always it has a finite number of values.

In some sciences the solution of equations is of paramount importance, but in the application of mathematics to statistics, solving for unknowns occurs far less often than working with variables.

Variable. Try to find a value of x for which the equation $(x+2)(x-2)=x^2-4$ is not true. You may let x represent any number you like, but the statement *always* holds for *all values* of x, large or small, integral or fractional, positive or negative, rational or irrational. Suppose we translate this equation into the question, "What is the number such that the product of two more than the number and two less than the number shall be four less than the square of the number?" The only possible answer to such a question is that this relationship is true for *all* numbers. A question is therefore a rather unsatisfactory translation for this equation. It is more meaningful to translate this equation as an observation, a statement of a universal relationship, true for any number one may choose. Here x is not an unknown but a variable.

Likewise, the following are true for all values of the variable. Translate each of these into words:

$$3n+7n-4n=6n$$
$$4(x+1) \quad =4x+4$$
$$(r+1)(r-1)=r^2-1$$
$$5(x+y) \quad =5x+5y$$
$$(n+2)^2 \quad =n^2+2n+4$$

Identity and Equation of Condition. The equation $\frac{x}{2}+\frac{x}{3}=10$ asks the question "What is the number whose half and third added together make ten?" or makes a conditional statement "Half of a number plus a third of that number will be 10 *if the number is 12*." The equation $17r+3r=20r$ asks no questions and makes an unconditional statement "When 17 times a number and 3 times that number are added, the result is always 20 times that number." The statement $\frac{x}{2}+\frac{x}{3}=10$ is true for one value of x only, the statement $17r+3r=20r$ is true for all values of r.

At first sight, the equation

$$(x-5)(x-1)+(x+2)(x-3)+3x+3=2(x-1)^2$$

looks as though it were an equation of condition, asking the values of x for which the equation is true. If both members are expanded, however, we have

$$x^2-6x+5+x^2-x-6+3x+3=2x^2-4x+2$$

in which the two members reduce to the same thing. Therefore the equation is an identity, true no matter what value x may have. Consequently x is here a variable rather than an unknown.

If an equation is true for a limited number of values, then it is an equation of condition, true only on condition that the unknown has a certain value or certain values.

Thus $3x-5=20$ is true if and only if $x=8\frac{1}{3}$.

$x^2+3x-54=0$ is true if $x=6$ or $x=-9$ and not otherwise.

$6x^3+11x^2-19x+6=0$ is true if $x=\frac{1}{2}$, $x=\frac{2}{3}$, or $x=-3$, and not otherwise.

Sometimes what looks like an equation has no finite solution. For example, there is no finite number for which

$$(x-3)(x-7)+4=x^2-10x.$$

If we attempt to solve this, we have

$$x^2-10x+21+4=x^2-10x$$
$$\text{and} \qquad 25=0.$$

The result is an absurdity. In other words, there is no finite number which can be substituted for x to satisfy the equation.

A single equation containing more than one unknown is indeterminate, satisfied by infinitely many sets of values. In general we must have as many equations as unknowns to obtain a unique solution. When we have fewer equations than unknowns, they are satisfied by an indefinitely large number of values. When we have more equations than unknowns, it often happens that no solution will satisfy them all. Thus there are infinitely many pairs of values of x and y such that $x-y=2$, but only one pair for which $x-y=2$ and $x+y=6$. That pair is $x=4$, $y=2$. Moreover there are no pairs for which $x-y=2$, $x+y=6$, and $2x+3y=10$.

Function. Write down several pairs of values for which the equation $y=x+3$ would be true. Translated into words this reads, "There are two numbers such that one is 3 units larger than the other." Obviously there are an unlimited number of pairs of values for which this relationship holds, and one can imagine values of x stretching away toward infinity in either direction, each one tied to a related value of y by the equation $y=x+3$. Clearly x and y are *related pairs of variables*, rather than unknowns. As soon as x is given a value, then the value of y is definitely fixed, and vice versa, i.e., y is a function of x. Obviously x is also a function of y.

Consider the equation $C=\frac{5}{9}(F-32°)$ which states the relationship between readings on Centigrade and Fahrenheit thermometers. Any change in the value of F produces a corresponding change in the value of C. The Centigrade reading is expressed as a function of the Fahrenheit reading. As the relationship is stated here we say that F is the *independent variable* and C the *dependent variable* because C is stated in terms of F. Also we say that C is an *explicit* function of F while F is an *implicit* function of C. If the same equation is transformed to read $F=\frac{9}{5}C+32°$, we have F an explicit function of C and C an implicit function of F. Now C has become the independent variable and F the dependent variable.

When two variables are so related that any change in the first produces a corresponding change in the second, then the second is said to be a function of the first. The notation used by mathematicians to express symbolically that "y is some function of x" is $y=f(x)$. When the expression $f(x)$ is encountered in a treatise in pure mathematics, at least in advanced mathematics, it may be understood to mean "a function of x." However when we see $f(x)$ or $f(x')^2$ or any similar expression in a textbook in elementary statistics, it means something quite different, as we saw in Chapter XIII. There $f(x')^2$ meant simply "the square of x' multiplied by the corresponding frequency f." To avoid any possible confusion, and because the functional notation is not commonly used in texts in elementary statistics, the functional notation will not be used here. The concept of functionality, that is the dependence of one variable upon another, however, is fundamental to any clear thinking in the field of statistics.

Suppose $y=\frac{2}{3}(x-3z+2w)$, then y is a function of the three variables x, z, and w together. The size of the corn crop is a function of temperature, rainfall, and other factors. The cost of a garment is a function of the quality of the cloth, the amount of cloth, the expense of manufacture, the expense of selling, and other factors. The weight of a child is a function of its age, sex, height, race, health, skeletal structure, and other factors. Statistical method is commonly applied to problems in which one variable is a function of many other variables.

Parameter. A parameter is a constant so long as you consider one particular situation, it is a variable when you generalize all such situations. For example, $y=3x$ represents a straight line through the origin with slope equal to 3; $y=\frac{1}{2}x$ represents a straight line through the origin with slope equal to $\frac{1}{2}$. What is represented by $y=-7x$? by $y=\frac{2}{3}x$? by $y=-\frac{9}{2}x$?

It is evident that these equations are alike except for the numerical coefficient of x, and that the lines are all straight lines through the origin, with varying slopes. We may generalize these equations with the single equation $y=mx$ in which m represents the variable slope of the line. A quantity used as m is used here is called a *parameter*.

In the section on graphs, we learned that such equations as $y=3x$, $y=3x-5$, $y=3x+2$, $y=3x+7$, represent parallel straight lines, and that the constants 0, -5, $+2$, 7, in these equations indicate the distance from the origin to the point at which the line cuts the y-axis. These equations may be generalized by the equation $y=3x+k$ representing the entire set of lines with slope 3. Such a set of lines is often called a "family." Here k is a parameter showing the distance from the origin to the intersection with the vertical axis. In the same fashion, $y=-2x+k$ represents the family of straight lines with slope -2, and $y=\frac{2}{3}x+k$ represents the family of straight lines with slope $\frac{2}{3}$.

If we wish to write an equation for a straight line in which both the slope and the intersection with the y-axis are generalized, we shall need two parameters. We may write $y=mx+k$, and may consider m and k to be parameters, variable constants changing from one equation to the next, while x and y are true variables. If we give m and k particular values, say $m=2$ and $k=-3$, then we have an equation, $y=2x-3$, representing a particular relationship between the variables x and y.

To generalize such quadratic equations as $y=3x^2+2x-1$, $y=x^2-\frac{5}{2}x+\frac{1}{2}$, or $y=-2x^2+\frac{1}{3}x-\frac{1}{4}$, requires three parameters. If we use a, b, and c as these parameters, the generalized equation is $y=ax^2+bx+c$. To generalize such equations as $y=3x-2w+4$, $y=4x+w-\frac{2}{3}$, $y=\frac{1}{3}x+\frac{2}{5}w-\frac{3}{4}$, requires three parameters, and the generalized equation may be written $y=ax+bw+c$.

Suppose that a spelling test S_1, a grammar test S_2, and a composition test S_3 have been given to all the children in grades 5 to 9 in a large city school system. The director of research wants a combined score on the three tests for each child, but he decides to weight the tests differently for each grade. For the total score he writes the equation

$$T = m_1 S_1 + m_2 S_2 + m_3 S_3 + k$$

where m_1, m_2, and m_3 are the multipliers by which he proposes to weight each score, and k is a number which he proposes to add to the composite in order to make the mean score for the various grades come out the same. Thus m_1, m_2, m_3, and k are parameters, varying from grade to grade but constant for all the children within a single grade. T, S_1, S_2, and S_3 vary from child to child and are genuine variables.

The investigator now undertakes a statistical study to determine what numerical values these parameters have in each particular grade. Until this study is completed these parameters are *unknowns*. T, S_1, S_2, and S_3, however, are not unknowns but variables. They are known for every child and furnish the statistical data from which values of the parameters may be computed. Such statistical procedures are outside the scope of the present discussion. Let us suppose, however, that in this study the investigator decides to weight his test scores in inverse proportion to the standard deviation of these scores, so that he lets $m_1 = \dfrac{1}{\sigma_1}$, $m_2 = \dfrac{1}{\sigma_2}$, and $m_3 = \dfrac{1}{\sigma_3}$. He now computes these standard deviations for each grade separately, and consequently the values of σ_1, σ_2, and σ_3 are seen to be parameters, varying from grade to grade, but constant for all the children in any one grade.

As a further example, suppose that an investigator is studying the weight of children in relationship to their height and age. For a group of American born white boys of ages 6 to 16 he derives by statistical methods an equation to predict weight from age and height. His general formula is

$$W = r_{wh.a} \frac{\sigma_{w.a}}{\sigma_{h.a}} H + r_{wa.h} \frac{\sigma_{w.h}}{\sigma_{a.h}} A + k$$

In this equation W, H, and A represent the height in inches, weight in pounds, and age in years of a particular child, differing from one child to the next, and are therefore variables, W being the dependent variable which is described as a function of the independent variables H and A. All the other letters in the equation, k, the two r's, and the four sigmas, represent statistical constants computed for the entire group of boys. Their precise meaning need not be understood, but it must be recognized that they are constants so far as this one group of boys is concerned. However if a similar study were made for Japanese boys, the relationships between height, weight, and age would be found to be slightly different and consequently these various r's, sigmas, and k would have slightly different numerical values. Likewise if the study were made for American born white girls, negro boys, negro girls, Swedish boys, Swedish girls, etc., these statistical constants would change from group to group. It is therefore apparent that W, H, and A are true variables while all the other letters represent parameters.

Equation and Function. The expression x^2+3x-5 is a function of x but it is not an equation because it contains no statement of equality. The expressions $x^2+3x-5=0$, $x^2+3x-5=y$, $x^2+3x-5=20$ are all equations because they state that two quantities are equal. The sign of equality performs a service similar to that of a verb in a sentence. "The broad road" is a phrase while "The road *is* broad" is a sentence. In the same way $2x^2$ is a function while $2x^2=8$ is an equation. Study the following:

Function or Phrase	Equation or Sentence
A stormy day	The day was stormy
A small boy	The small boy was playing marbles
My hat	The hat is mine
x^2-4x	$x^2-4x=40$
$3+12x-2x^2$	$3+12x-2x^2=y-5$
$4rs-2r+s^2$	$4rs+s^2=2r$
$(x-y)(x+y)$	$(x-y)(x+y)=x^2-y^2$

Exercise 25

1. From the list of algebraic expressions given below, select all those which are functions but not equations, and place a check in column 1 opposite each of these. In the same manner, place a check in column 2 opposite each expression which is an equation, a check in column 3 opposite each expression which is a conditional equation, a check in column 4 opposite each expression which is an identity.

Expression	Function but not an Equation	Equation	Conditional Equation	Identity
	1	2	3	4
(1) $x+y=30$				
(2) $y=x^2-3x+2$				
(3) $xy+3$				
(4) x^3+3x^2-2x-7				
(5) $x^3+3x^2-2x=7$				
(6) 49				
(7) $49x$				
(8) $3x+7y-4w$				
(9) $5(x-3)^2+4$				
(10) $2x+5x=7x$				
(11) $13(x-y)+7(x-y)$ $=20(x-y)$				
(12) $x=4y+10$				
(13) $x^2-7x+10=0$				
(14) $3(x-2)=3x-6$				
(15) $(x-3)(x+3)=x^2-9$				

2. On the line at the left of each equation, write a number to indicate how many values of the variable will satisfy that equation. Use the symbol ∞ when the number of values is unlimited.

——— (1) $2y+12=5y-3$

——— (2) $8y+6=8y+4$

——— (3) $17n-3n=14n$

——— (4) $2x^2-11x+6=0$

——— (5) $3x^3-5x^2+x=0$

——— (6) $x^4-4x^3+6x^2-4x+1=0$

——— (7) $5(x-2)+3(x-2)=8(x-2)$

——— (8) $y=x^2$

——— (9) $x+y=10$

———(10) $(x-2)(x+5)=x^2+3x-10$

———(11) $\dfrac{x^2}{x-2}+4=x+\dfrac{2(3x-4)}{x-2}$

———(12) $3x+5y=40$

———(13) $8x^2+10=8(x+1)(x-1)$

———(14) $y^6-y^4=20$

———(15) $x^2-3x+2=y$

———(16) $n-8=3$

———(17) $2x^2-11x+6=0$

———(18) $3(x-1)+5(x-1)=4(x-1)$

3. Each of the formulas given below is the statement of the way in which two or more variables are related. Each formula also contains one or more parameters. In each formula, decide which letters represent variables and which represent parameters.

(1) $C=r\left(\dfrac{\sigma_c}{\sigma_t}\right)T+M_c-r\left(\dfrac{\sigma_c}{\sigma_t}\right)M_t$

This formula is intended to estimate a student's most probable standing on a college algebra test (C) when his standing on a prognostic test (T) is known.

r is a measure of the relationship between scores on the two tests, computed for the entire class.

σ_c and σ_t are the standard deviations of the entire class on the two tests.

M_c and M_t are the mean scores of the entire class on the two tests.

(2) $S = m_1 T_1 + m_2 T_2 + m_3 T_3$, where S is the final score of a student, T_1, T_2, and T_3 are his scores on three separate tests, and m_1, m_2, and m_3 are the multipliers by which the separate scores are weighted to form the composite S. The formula is to apply to all students in a class.

(3) $T = \dfrac{S_1}{\sigma_1} + \dfrac{S_2}{\sigma_2} + \dfrac{S_3}{\sigma_3}$, where S_1, S_2, and S_3 are the scores made by a pupil on three separate tests, T is his total weighted score, and σ_1, σ_2, and σ_3 are the standard deviations of the scores of the entire class on the three tests.

XV

MULTIPLICATION OF POLYNOMIALS

INITIAL TEST

Expand each of these products mentally, write the results and compare with the answers in the key.

1. $(n-1)^2$

2. $(1-3a)^2$

3. $(4-5r)^2$

4. $(y-rx)^2$

5. $(x_1-2)(x_2+3)$

6. $(3a+5)^2$

7. $(3r-4n)^2$

8. $(a-2n)(2a+n)$

9. $\left(b-\dfrac{c}{d}\right)\left(\dfrac{a}{b}-\dfrac{c}{x}\right)$

10. $(x_1-a_1)(x_2-a_2)$

11. $\left(x_1-r_{12}\dfrac{\sigma_1}{\sigma_2}x_2\right)^2$

12. $\left(\dfrac{x}{a}-\dfrac{b}{c}\right)\left(\dfrac{a}{b}-\dfrac{c}{x}\right)$

13. $\left(n-\dfrac{p}{q}\right)\left(n+\dfrac{p}{q}\right)$

14. $(ax_1-\tfrac{2}{3}x_2)(ax_2+\tfrac{3}{2}x_1)$

15. $\left(x_1-r_{12}\dfrac{\sigma_1}{\sigma_2}x_2\right)\left(x_2-r_{12}\dfrac{\sigma_2}{\sigma_1}x_1\right)$

Importance. The derivation of many of the simpler statistical formulas calls for finding the product of two binomials, while more thorough study of statistical theory gives many occasions for finding higher powers of a binomial or powers of a polynomial. Since this book is not intended as background for advanced statistical work, it seems best to include here only such exercises in the multiplication of two binomials as are needed for the chapter on Summation.

Multiplication of Two Polynomials. This is obviously only an extension of the multiplication of a polynomial by a monomial, studied in Chapter VIII. To multiply $(3a-2b+c)$ by $(a-2c)$ we multiply it first by a, then by $-2c$, and add the results, thus:

141

$$
\begin{array}{l}
3a \ -2b \ +c \\
\underline{\quad a \ -2c} \\
3a^2-2ab+ac \\
\underline{\qquad\qquad -6ac+4bc-2c^2} \\
3a^2-2ab-5ac+4bc-2c^2
\end{array}
$$

EXERCISE 26

1. $(n-2r+5s)(s-3n+r)$
2. $(p-5q)(2p+q-1)$
3. $(c-1)(c^2-2c+1)$
4. $(a+b-1)(a-b+2)$
5. $(x^2-2xy+y^2)(x^2-2xy+y^2)$

Special Products of Binomials. The product of two binomials can be readily found by inspection without setting down the work on paper. It is obvious that $(a+b)(c+d)$ $=ab+ac+bc+bd$, no two of the four terms being similar. When some of the terms are similar and can be combined, as in $(a+2)(a-7)=a^2+2a-7a-14=a^2-5a-14$, there are various short cuts and special cases which usually receive a good deal of attention in a regular text in algebra. So far as the student of statistics is concerned, he can get on very well without knowing these special cases. He would not be much inconvenienced if he were obliged to write out the product of two binomials in four terms, subsequently combining similar terms when possible.

The student who prefers to master these short cuts should verify the following typical products by multiplication:

$$(a+b)^2=a^2+2ab+b^2$$
$$(a-b)^2=a^2-2ab+b^2$$
$$(a+b)(a-b)=a^2-b^2$$
$$(a+b)(a+c)=a^2+(b+c)a+bc$$
$$(m_1a+n_1b)(m_2a+n_2b)=m_1m_2a^2+(m_1n_2+m_2n_1)ab+n_1n_2b^2$$

With these types as patterns, the products in Exercise 27 can be written out by inspection. However, learning these types is of very little importance, and the student will do quite as well to write out the products in four terms and later combine similar terms.

EXERCISE 27

1. $(3-x_1)^2$

2. $(y-4a)(y-6a)$

3. $(2r-5)(2r+5)$

4. $(1-3c)^2$

5. $(h_1-h_2h_3)(h_1+h_2h_3)$

6. $(1-R_{1.23}^2)^2$

7. $\left(\dfrac{a}{b}-\dfrac{c}{d}\right)\left(\dfrac{b}{a}+d\right)$

8. $(x_2-a_2)(x_3-a_3)$

9. $\left(y-r_{xy}\dfrac{\sigma_y}{\sigma_x}x\right)^2$

10. $\left(y-r\dfrac{\sigma_y}{\sigma_x}x\right)\left(x-r\dfrac{\sigma_x}{\sigma_y}y\right)$

11. $(4n-5p)(3n+2p)$

12. $(3t+1)(2-5t)$

13. $(1-5x)(5x+1)$

14. $(r_1-n_1)(r_1+2n_1)$

15. $(x'-c)^2$

16. $(X-M)^2$

17. $(X-M_x)(Y-M_y)$

18. $(x'-c_x)(y'-c_y)$

19. $\left(x_2-r_{23}\dfrac{\sigma_2}{\sigma_3}x_3\right)\left(x_4-r_{34}\dfrac{\sigma_4}{\sigma_3}x_3\right)$

20. $\left(x_5-r_{35}\dfrac{\sigma_5}{\sigma_3}x_3\right)^2$

SECOND TEST

Expand each of these products mentally, write the results, and compare with the answers in the key.

1. $(1-r^2)^2$

2. $(3d+1)^2$

3. $(2-rx)^2$

4. $(x_1-r_{12}x_2)^2$

5. $(y_1-7)(y_2+1)$

6. $(4c-3)^2$

7. $(5p-2q)^2$

8. $(r-3t)(3t+r)$

9. $\left(x-\dfrac{a}{n}\right)\left(\dfrac{n}{x}-\dfrac{x}{a}\right)$

10. $(y_1-c_1)(y_2-c_2)$

11. $\left(x_3-r_{13}\dfrac{\sigma_3}{\sigma_1}x_1\right)^2$

12. $\left(\dfrac{n}{2}-\dfrac{1}{3}\right)\left(\dfrac{2}{3}-\dfrac{n}{2}\right)$

13. $\left(c-\dfrac{r}{n}\right)\left(c+\dfrac{r}{n}\right)$

14. $(\tfrac{2}{3}x_1-1)(\tfrac{2}{3}x_1-2)$

15. $\left(y_1-r_{12}\dfrac{\sigma_1}{\sigma_2}y_2\right)\left(y_3-r_{23}\dfrac{\sigma_3}{\sigma_2}y_2\right)$

XVI

FACTORING, SUMMATION

INITIAL TEST

1. Factor each of the following expressions into a monomial and a polynomial factor:

(1) $ax_1 + ax_2 + ax_3$

(2) $\sigma_1^2 - \sigma_1^2 r_{12}^2$

(3) $bx_1y_1 + bx_2y_2 + bx_3y_3 + bx_4y_4$

(4) $6rn - 3tn + 3n^2$

(5) $\sigma_1^2 + r_{12}\sigma_1\sigma_2 + r_{13}\sigma_1\sigma_3$

(6) $A_1b + A_2b + A_3b$

(7) $p_1q_1n + p_2q_2n + p_3q_3n$

(8) $\sigma_2^2 + \sigma_2 R_{2.3}$

(9) $\dfrac{a}{n} + \dfrac{b}{n} + \dfrac{c}{n}$

(10) $r_1x + r_2x + r_3x$

(11) $5a^2 + 5b^2 + 5c^2$

(12) $Na + Nb$

2. Assume that x and y represent variables and all other letters represent constants, and that N is the number of terms to be added in each summation. Place a plus sign in front of each statement which you consider to be correct and a minus sign in front of each statement which you consider to be incorrect.

———— (1) $\Sigma y = Ny$

———— (2) $\Sigma b = Nb$

———— (3) $\Sigma kx^2 = Nkx^2$

———— (4) $\Sigma kx^2 = k\Sigma x^2$

———— (5) $\Sigma R_{1.2}^2 xy = R_{1.2}^2 \Sigma xy$

———— (6) $\Sigma(x-y) = \Sigma x - \Sigma y$

———— (7) $\Sigma xy = y\Sigma x$

———— (8) $\Sigma 3c = 3Nc$

———— (9) $\Sigma(2x)(5y) = 10\Sigma xy$

————(10) $\Sigma(y+1) = \Sigma y + N$

————(11) $\Sigma ny = n\Sigma y$

————(12) $\Sigma ny = y\Sigma n$

144

————(13) $\Sigma xy = x \Sigma y$

————(14) $\Sigma (x-3)^2 = \Sigma x^2 - 6\Sigma x + 9N$

————(15) $\Sigma (M-x) = NM - \Sigma x$

————(16) $\Sigma (x-1) = Nx - N$

————(17) $\Sigma xy = Nxy$

————(18) $\Sigma 5x = 5\Sigma x$

————(19) $\Sigma cxy = x\Sigma cy$

————(20) $\Sigma \sigma^2 xy = \sigma^2 \Sigma xy$

3. In the following problems it is to be understood that x with any subscript whatever, or x without a subscript, represents a variable. Any other letter represents a parameter or constant. The following substitutions may be made:

$$\Sigma x = 0$$

$$\frac{1}{N}\Sigma x_1^2 = \sigma_1^2$$

$$\frac{1}{N}\Sigma x_1 x_2 = r_{12}\sigma_1\sigma_2 = r_{21}\sigma_1\sigma_2$$

Similar substitutions may be made for other subscripts, as for example $\frac{1}{N}\Sigma x_4^2 = \sigma_4^2$, $\quad \frac{\Sigma x_2 x_4}{N\sigma_2\sigma_4} = r_{24}$, etc.

Perform whatever algebraic manipulations and substitutions are necessary, and for each of the following expressions find an equivalent expression in which the letter x does not appear.

(1) $\frac{1}{N}\Sigma (x_1 - c)(x_2 - b)$

(2) $\frac{1}{N}\Sigma \left(x_1 - r_{12}\frac{\sigma_1}{\sigma_2}x_2 \right)^2$

(3) $\frac{1}{N}\Sigma \left(x_1 - r_{12}\frac{\sigma_1}{\sigma_2}x_2 \right)\left(x_3 - r_{23}\frac{\sigma_3}{\sigma_2}x_2 \right)$

Importance. The chief necessity for factoring in elementary statistical method is in connection with problems involving summation, which often involve taking out a monomial factor. Such problems of summation are of the utmost importance to statistics. It often happens also that a monomial factor is taken out in order to reduce formulas to simpler form. Factoring polynomials into binomial or trinomial factors is seldom needed.

Monomial Factor. In the chapter on Signed Numbers, page 61, we had examples in which a polynomial was to be divided by a monomial. To find a monomial factor of a polynomial is the same thing, except that you have to determine by inspection what monomial will make a satisfactory divisor. Ordinarily it is convenient to select the largest monomial which will divide each term of the polynomial and leave the various quotient terms all integers. This is, however, not always the most satisfactory divisor to use in a particular situation. If asked to factor the expression $24a^2x - 18ax^2 + 30ax$, most people would think of $6ax(4a - 3x + 5)$, but other possible sets of factors would be $3a(8ax - 6x^2 + 10x)$, or $6x(4a^2 - 3ax + 5a)$, or $12ax(2a - \frac{3}{2}x + \frac{5}{2})$, and so on indefinitely.

The monomial factor may be a fraction.

Thus $\dfrac{a^2x}{r} - \dfrac{2ay}{r} + \dfrac{ax}{r} = \dfrac{a}{r}(ax - 2y + x)$,

and $\dfrac{5n}{2} + 10n^2 - \dfrac{15n^3}{2} = \dfrac{5n}{2}(1 + 4n - 3n^2)$

Subscript. It is not necessary in this connection for the student to know what a particular subscript connotes, but merely to recognize that it is or is not like some other subscript. One of the noteworthy aspects of purely algebraic work is that algebraic manipulation may be successfully carried out by a person who is entirely ignorant of the meaning attached to the symbols. Thus suppose you need to factor $R_{1.23}r_{12} + R_{2.13}r_{12} - R_{1.23}R_{2.13}r_{12}$ you do not need to have any idea of the concepts back of these rather complicated looking subscripts in order to see that r_{12} (whatever it means) is a common factor and $R_{1.23}$ and $R_{2.13}$ have subscripts which presumably do not mean the same. You will therefore write

$$R_{1.23}r_{12} + R_{2.13}r_{12} - R_{1.23}R_{2.13}r_{12} = r_{12}(R_{1.23} + R_{2.13} - R_{1.23}R_{2.13}).$$

Exercise 28

Factor each of the following expressions. (While there are conceivably an infinite variety of correct answers, those given in the key are the result of taking out the largest monomial factor which leaves integral terms in the polynomial.)

1. $5a_1 + 10a_2 + 25a_3$
2. $4ab + 4bc + 4ac$
3. $\dfrac{ab}{3} + \dfrac{ac}{3} + \dfrac{ad}{3}$
4. $ab_1 + ab_2 + ab_3$
5. $a_1b + a_2b + a_3b$
6. $2r_{12}r_{13} + 4r_{15}r_{13}$
7. $\sigma_1^2 + r_1\sigma_1^2 + r_1^2\sigma_1^2$
8. $n_1x + n_2x + n_3x + n_4x$
9. $NM_1 + NM_2 + NM_3$
10. $2k + 2k^2 + 4k^3$

11. $\sigma_1^2 - \sigma_1^2n_{12}^2$
12. $\dfrac{p}{q} + \dfrac{p^2}{q^2}$
13. $ax_1y_1 + ax_2y_2 + ax_3y_3$
14. $at_1 + at_2 + at_3$
15. $at_1s_1 + at_2s_2 + at_3s_3$
16. $a_1ts + a_2ts + a_3ts$
17. $cx_1x_2 + cx_1x_3 + cx_2x_3$
18. $nX_1 + nX_2 + nX_3$
19. $p_1q_1r + p_2q_2r + p_3q_3r$
20. $r_1\sqrt{1 - r_1^2} - 2r_2\sqrt{1 - r_1^2}$

Summation. Suppose that $h_1, h_2 \ldots h_{20}$ are the heights (in inches) of twenty boys. To find the mean, or average height, we would add these and divide the result by twenty.

$$\text{Mean} = \frac{1}{20}(h_1 + h_2 + h_3 + \cdots + h_{18} + h_{19} + h_{20}).$$

This sum may be more concisely expressed by the symbol Σh, read "the sum of the h's." Σ is the large *sigma* of the Greek alphabet, comparable to our capital S. To indicate that the sum extends only from h_1 to h_{20}, a more careful manner of writing would place a small 1 below the summation sign and a small 20 above it, thus $\sum\limits_{i=1}^{i=20} h_i$. In complicated problems this is necessary to avoid confusion. To a mathematician the practice of failing to indicate the limits of summation seems careless and slipshod. However, in elementary statistics the summation is almost always over the first N cases, whereas in purely mathematical problems, or in more advanced theory of statistics, the limits may be quite different. Consequently in elementary statistics the limits of summation are commonly not written and are understood to be from 1 to N.

To clarify the concept, the student should expand a number of such sums into polynomials. First study the following illustrations and then the problems in Exercise 29.

Illustrations:

(1) $\sum\limits_{i=1}^{i=6}(x_i^2+k) = (x_1^2+k)+(x_2^2+k)+(x_3^2+k)+(x_4^2+k)$

$\qquad +(x_5^2+k)+(x_6^2+k)=(x_1^2+x_2^2+x_3^2+x_4^2+x_5^2+x_6^2)+6k$

(Since the numbers above and below the summation sign state that the subscript for x changes from 1 to 6 but do not mention k, we must assume that k is a constant.)

(2) $\sum\limits_{i=1}^{i=5} ax_iy_i = ax_1y_1+ax_2y_2+ax_3y_3+ax_4y_4+ax_5y_5$

$\qquad = a(x_1y_1+x_2y_2+x_3y_3+x_4y_4+x_5y_5)$

(3) $\sum\limits_{i=3}^{i=7}(x_i+a)^2 = \sum\limits_{i=3}^{i=7}(x_i^2+2ax_i+a^2) = (x_3^2+2ax_3+a^2)$

$\qquad +(x_4^2+2ax_4+a^2)+(x_5^2+2ax_5+a^2)+(x_6^2+2ax_6+a^2)$

$\qquad\qquad\qquad\qquad\qquad\qquad +(x_7^2+2ax_7+a^2)$

$\qquad = (x_3^2+x_4^2+x_5^2+x_6^2+x_7^2)+2a(x_3+x_4+x_5+x_6+x_7)+5a^2$

$$(4)\quad \sum_{i=1}^{i=N}(x_i-1)(y_i-2) = \sum_{i=1}^{i=N}(x_iy_i-y_i-2x_i+2)$$

$$= (x_1y_1-y_1-2x_1+2)+(x_2y_2-y_2-2x_2+2)$$
$$+(x_3y_3-y_3-2x_3+2)+\cdots+(x_Ny_N-y_N-2x_N+2)$$
$$= (x_1y_1+x_2y_2+\cdots+x_Ny_N)-(y_1+y_2+\cdots+y_N)$$
$$-2(x_1+x_2\cdots+x_N)+2N$$

In the next three illustrations the limits of summation are understood to be from 1 to N. The letters x, y, z, w are understood to represent variables, changing from term to term in the summation because they vary from individual to individual. All other letters are understood to represent constants, which do not change from one individual to another but are the same for all members of the group being studied.

$$(5)\quad \Sigma(x-ay)^2 = \Sigma(x^2-2axy+a^2y^2) = (x_1^2-2ax_1y_1+a^2y_1^2)$$
$$+(x_2^2-2ax_2y_2+a^2y_2^2)+\cdots+(x_N^2-2ax_Ny_N+a^2y_N^2)$$
$$= (x_1^2+x_2^2+\cdots+x_N^2)-2a(x_1y_1+x_2y_2+\cdots$$
$$+x_Ny_N)+a^2(y_1^2+y_2^2+\cdots+y_N^2)$$

$$(6)\quad \Sigma(w+1)=(w_1+1)+(w_2+1)+(w_3+1)+\cdots+(w_N+1)$$
$$= w_1+w_2+\cdots+w_N+N$$

$$(7)\quad \Sigma a(x-cz)=a(x_1-cz_1)+a(x_2-cz_2)+\cdots+a(x_N-xz_N)$$
$$= ax_1+ax_2+\cdots+ax_N-acz_1-acz_2-\cdots-acz_N$$
$$= a(x_1+x_2+\cdots x_N)-ac(z_1+z_2+\cdots+z_N)$$

Exercise 29

Expand the following summations and group the resulting terms into groups of similar terms, as in the preceding illustrations. When no limits are indicated it is assumed that the summation extends from 1 to N and that x, y, z, and w are variables and all other letters constants.

1. $\displaystyle\sum_{i=1}^{i=4} f_i x_i y_i$

2. Σax

3. $\Sigma(w+c)$

4. $\displaystyle\sum_{i=5}^{i=7} (y_i-c)^2$

5. $\Sigma 3(z+a)$

6. $\displaystyle\sum_{i=6}^{i=9} (z_i-tw_i)^2$

7. $\Sigma w(x-a)^2$

8. $\displaystyle\sum_{i=9}^{i=12} (x_i+a)(y_i+b)$

9. $\Sigma(x-bw)^2$

10. $\Sigma(x-c_x)(y-c_y)$

Language. A mathematician might speak of Σx as "Sigma x", but a statistician would ordinarily say "Summation x", or "The sum of the x's". The statistician is likely to avoid calling the summation sign by its Greek name because he also makes continual use of the small Greek sigma, σ, in a very different connection, and to call them both "sigma" would be highly confusing. When a statistician says "sigma x" he usually means σ_x and not Σx.

The terms immediately following a summation sign are under its influence, while those preceding it are outside its influence. Thus in the expression $a\Sigma(x+y)$, x and y are "under" the summation sign while a is "outside" the sign.

Rules for Summation. Certain patterns in these expansions should now be apparent. Reference to the seven illustrations on pages 148 and 149 shows that they might be written thus:

1. $\Sigma(x^2+k)=\Sigma x^2+Nk$
2. $\Sigma axy=a\Sigma xy$
3. $\Sigma(x+a)^2=\Sigma(x^2+2ax+a^2)=\Sigma x^2+2a\Sigma x+Na^2$
4. $\Sigma(x-1)(y-2)=\Sigma(xy-2x-y+2)=\Sigma xy-2\Sigma x-\Sigma y+2N$
5. $\Sigma(x-ay)^2=\Sigma(x^2-2axy+a^2y^2)=\Sigma x^2-2a\Sigma xy+a^2\Sigma y^2$
6. $\Sigma(w+1)=\Sigma w+N$
7. $\Sigma a(x-cz)=\Sigma(ax-acz)=a\Sigma x-ac\Sigma z$

A careful study of these illustrations and of Exercise 29 suggests the following rules:

1. *The summation of a polynomial may be obtained by summing the terms separately.* $\Sigma(x+y+z)=\Sigma x+\Sigma y+\Sigma z$.

2. *The summation of a variable times a constant may be obtained by multiplying the constant by the summation of the variable.* $\Sigma ax=a\Sigma x$ *but not* $x\Sigma a$.

3. *The summation for N terms of a constant is N times that constant.* $\Sigma a=Na$.

4. *The summation of the product of two variables is not equal to the product of one variable and the summation of the other.*

EXERCISE 30

Apply the rules for summation to change the form of the following expressions, assuming x, x', y, and w to represent variables and all other letters to represent constants.

1. $\Sigma(x+2y+1)$
2. $\Sigma(x-c)(y-c)$
3. $\Sigma(x-a)^2$
4. $\Sigma a(x-ay)$
5. $\Sigma(x-dw)^2$
6. $\Sigma(x-c)^3$
7. $\Sigma(x'-x+a)$
8. $\Sigma w(y-b)^2$
9. Σa
10. $\Sigma(w+c)$
11. Σab
12. $\Sigma a(x-1)$

A Different Use of Subscripts. In the early portions of this chapter we have used subscripts to distinguish among the N members of a group. This was a device which helped the thinking of persons unaccustomed to summation. In Exercise 30 however you have thrown away this crutch and are now thinking easily without the necessity of expanding your summations into polynomials in which subscripts serve to distinguish the various terms. Now we are about to use subscripts for a slightly different purpose. Instead of using H, W, and A to stand for the height, weight, and age of a child, we might use X_H, X_W, and X_A, or we might use X', X'', and X''' as the names of these three variables, or X_1, X_2, and X_3. The latter form has much to recommend it, particularly in complicated formulas dealing with many variables. For example, suppose

$X_1 = $ Height $\qquad$ Then $M_1 = \dfrac{\Sigma X_1}{N} = $ mean height of the group

$X_2 = $ Weight $\qquad\qquad M_2 = \dfrac{\Sigma X_2}{N} = $ mean weight of the group

$X_3 = $ Age $\qquad\qquad\quad M_3 = \dfrac{\Sigma X_3}{N} = $ mean age of the group

$$\sigma_1 = \sqrt{\frac{\Sigma x_1^2}{N}} = \text{standard deviation of height}$$

$$\sigma_2 = \sqrt{\frac{\Sigma x_2^2}{N}} = \text{standard deviation of weight}$$

$$\sigma_3 = \sqrt{\frac{\Sigma x_3^2}{N}} = \text{standard deviation of age}$$

Derivation of Statistical Formulas. Most of the important formulas of statistics are obtained through some process of summation. The process of derivation may be entirely clear to a mathematician who has no idea what the symbols stand for or how the formulas should be used when obtained. Some of the simpler formulas will now be derived as an exercise in algebraic summation. It is not expected that the symbols used shall have any concrete meaning for the student or that he shall understand the statistical concepts back of these expressions, but merely that he shall follow through the process as an exercise in algebra. In the examples which follow, the use of the formula has been suggested merely for convenience of reference in case someone who has studied statistical method wishes to look up a derivation here. The person studying this material before he has had a course in statistical method need pay no attention to these statements concerning the nature of the formulas.

In the chapter on Symbolism in Statistics these relations were used:

$$x_1 = X_1 - M_1 \qquad \Sigma x_1 = 0$$

$$M_1 = \frac{\Sigma X_1}{N}$$

$$\sigma_1 = \sqrt{\frac{\Sigma x_1^2}{N}} \quad \text{or} \quad \sigma_1^2 = \frac{\Sigma x_1^2}{N}$$

$$x_1' = x_1 + c_1$$

We will now make use of the further definitions:

$$r_{12} = \frac{\Sigma x_1 x_2}{N \sigma_1 \sigma_2} \quad \text{or} \quad r_{12} \sigma_1 \sigma_2 = \frac{\Sigma x_1 x_2}{N}$$

$$r_{12} = r_{21}$$

When only one variable occurs in a problem, subscripts may be omitted. Similar definitions will of course hold for other subscripts, as

$$\frac{\Sigma x_2 x_3}{N} = r_{23} \sigma_2 \sigma_3, \quad r_{45} = \frac{\Sigma x_4 x_5}{N \sigma_4 \sigma_5}, \quad \Sigma x_3^2 = N \sigma_3^2, \text{ etc.}$$

In the derivation of statistical formulas on pages 154 to 158 as well as in Exercise 31 it is to be understood that x and X, either with or without a subscript, represent variables, while all other letters represent constants.

EXERCISE 31

Write an equivalent expression which might be substituted for each of the following:

1. $\dfrac{\Sigma X_2}{N}$

2. ΣX_2

3. $\dfrac{\Sigma x_3^2}{N}$

4. $\dfrac{\Sigma x_2 x_3}{N}$

5. Σx_4^2

6. $\Sigma c x_1$

7. $\Sigma 5 x_2$

8. $\dfrac{\Sigma x_1 x_3}{N}$

9. $\Sigma x_3 x_4$

10. $\Sigma x_1 x_4$

11. $\Sigma b x_2^2$

12. ΣX_3

15. $\dfrac{\Sigma a x_1 x_2}{N}$

18. $\dfrac{1}{N}\Sigma r_{12}\dfrac{\sigma_1}{\sigma_2}$

13. $\Sigma a x_3$

16. $\dfrac{\Sigma c x}{N}$

19. $\dfrac{1}{N}\Sigma r\dfrac{\sigma_2}{\sigma_3}x_3^2$

14. $\dfrac{1}{N}\Sigma r_{12}x_1$

17. $\dfrac{\Sigma r_{12}x_1 x_2}{N}$

20. $\dfrac{1}{N}\Sigma r_{32}\dfrac{\sigma_3}{\sigma_2}x_1 x_2$

Examples of Deriving Statistical Formulas

1. To show that $c=\dfrac{\Sigma x'}{N}$

(This is the formula for the correction to be made to an assumed mean. See chapter on Statistical Symbolism.)

We have already made use of the relationship $\quad x'=x+c$

Summing this gives us $\quad \Sigma x'=\Sigma x+Nc$

But we know that $\Sigma x=0$, therefore $\quad \Sigma x'=Nc$

Solving this for c, gives us $\quad c=\dfrac{\Sigma x'}{N}$

2. To show that
$$\sigma=\sqrt{\dfrac{\Sigma(x')^2}{N}-c^2}$$

(This is the formula for computing σ from an assumed mean.)

As before $\qquad\qquad\quad x'=x+c$

Squaring both sides, $\quad (x')^2=x^2+2cx+c^2$

Summing, $\qquad \Sigma(x')^2=\Sigma x^2+2c\Sigma x+Nc^2$

But $\Sigma x=0$ $\qquad \Sigma(x')^2=\Sigma x^2+Nc^2$

Dividing by N, $\qquad \dfrac{\Sigma(x')^2}{N}=\dfrac{\Sigma x^2}{N}+c^2$

Transposing $\qquad \dfrac{\Sigma x^2}{N}=\dfrac{(\Sigma x')^2}{N}-c^2$

Taking square root of both sides $\qquad \sqrt{\dfrac{\Sigma x^2}{N}}=\sqrt{\dfrac{\Sigma(x')^2}{N}-c^2}$

Since by definition
$$\sigma=\sqrt{\frac{\Sigma x^2}{N}}, \quad \text{therefore} \quad \sigma=\sqrt{\frac{\Sigma(x')^2}{N}-c^2} \text{ also.}$$

3. To show that
$$\sigma=\sqrt{\frac{\Sigma X^2}{N}-M^2}$$

(This is the "gross score" formula for computing σ.)

By definition of symbols,

$$x=X-M$$

Squaring

$$x^2=X^2-2MX+M^2$$

Summing

$$\Sigma x^2=\Sigma X^2-2M\Sigma X+NM^2$$

But $\Sigma X=NM$

$$\Sigma x^2=\Sigma X^2-2NM^2+NM^2$$

Or

$$\frac{\Sigma x^2}{N}=\frac{\Sigma X^2}{N}-M^2$$

Taking square root,

$$\sqrt{\frac{\Sigma x^2}{N}}=\sqrt{\frac{\Sigma X^2}{N}-M^2}$$

Therefore

$$\sigma=\sqrt{\frac{\Sigma X^2}{N}-M^2}$$

4. To show that $\frac{1}{N}\Sigma\left(x_2-r_{23}\frac{\sigma_2}{\sigma_3}x_3\right)^2=\sigma_2^2(1-r_{23}^2)$.   (This is

closely related to a formula known as the "standard error of estimate.")

First we must expand the square of the binomial

$$\frac{1}{N}\Sigma\left(x_2-r_{23}\frac{\sigma_2}{\sigma_3}x_3\right)^2$$

$$=\frac{1}{N}\Sigma\left(x_2^2-2r_{23}\frac{\sigma_2}{\sigma_3}x_2x_3\right.$$

$$\left.+r_{23}^2\frac{\sigma_2^2}{\sigma_3^2}x_3^2\right)$$

Then we write the result as the sum of three separate summations

$$= \frac{\Sigma x_2^2}{N} - 2r_{23}\frac{\sigma_2}{\sigma_3}\frac{\Sigma x_2 x_3}{N}$$
$$+ r_{23}^2 \frac{\sigma_2^2}{\sigma_3^2}\frac{\Sigma x_3^2}{N}$$

Then we make substitutions similar to those in Exercise 31

$$= \sigma_2^2 - 2r_{23}\frac{\sigma_2}{\sigma_3}(r_{23}\sigma_2\sigma_3)$$
$$+ r_{23}^2 \frac{\sigma_2^2}{\sigma_3^2}(\sigma_3^2)$$

And reduce the result

$$= \sigma_2^2 - 2r_{23}^2\sigma_2^2 + r_{23}^2\sigma_2^2$$
$$= \sigma_2^2 - r_{23}^2\sigma_2^2$$

And factoring, we have

$$= \sigma_2^2(1 - r_{23}^2)$$

5. To show that $\frac{1}{N}\Sigma x_1 x_2 = \frac{1}{N}\Sigma x_1' x_2' - c_1 c_2$ (This is the numerator of a formula often used for computing the coefficient of correlation.)

We have already assumed the relationship and

$$x_1' = x_1 + c_1$$
$$x_2' = x_2 + c_2$$

Multiplying these two expressions and expanding the product,

$$x_1' x_2' = (x_1 + c_1)(x_2 + c_2)$$

$$x_1' x_2' = x_1 x_2 + c_1 x_2 + c_2 x_1 + c_1 c_2$$

Summing,

$$\Sigma x_1' x_2' = \Sigma x_1 x_2 + c_1 \Sigma x_2$$
$$+ c_2 \Sigma x_1 + N c_1 c_2$$

But $\Sigma x_2 = 0$ and $\Sigma x_1 = 0$,

$$\Sigma x_1' x_2' = \Sigma x_1 x_2 + N c_1 c_2$$

Dividing by N and transposing

$$\frac{1}{N}\Sigma x_1 x_2 = \frac{1}{N}\Sigma x_1' x_2' - c_1 c_2$$

6. To show that $\frac{1}{N}\Sigma(x_3 - x_4)^2 = \sigma_3^2 - 2r_{34}\sigma_3\sigma_4 + \sigma_4^2$ (This is the square of what is called "the standard error of a difference".)

$$\frac{1}{N}\Sigma(x_3-x_4)^2=\frac{1}{N}\Sigma(x_3^2-2x_3x_4+x_4^2)$$
$$=\frac{\Sigma x_3^2}{N}-2\frac{\Sigma x_3x_4}{N}+\frac{\Sigma x_4^2}{N}$$
$$=\sigma_3^2-2r_{34}\sigma_3\sigma_4+\sigma_4^2$$

7. To show that

$$\frac{1}{N}\Sigma\left(x_1-r_{13}\frac{\sigma_1}{\sigma_3}x_3\right)\left(x_2-r_{23}\frac{\sigma_2}{\sigma_3}x_3\right)=\sigma_1\sigma_2(r_{12}-r_{13}r_{23})$$

(This is part of the formula for a "partial correlation coefficient".)

$$\frac{1}{N}\Sigma\left(x_1-r_{13}\frac{\sigma_1}{\sigma_3}x_3\right)\left(x_2-r_{23}\frac{\sigma_2}{\sigma_3}x_3\right)$$
$$=\frac{1}{N}\Sigma\left(x_1x_2-r_{13}\frac{\sigma_1}{\sigma_3}x_2x_3-r_{23}\frac{\sigma_2}{\sigma_3}x_1x_3+r_{13}r_{23}\frac{\sigma_1\sigma_2}{\sigma_3^2}x_3^2\right)$$
$$=\frac{\Sigma x_1x_2}{N}-r_{13}\frac{\sigma_1}{\sigma_3}\frac{\Sigma x_2x_3}{N}-r_{23}\frac{\sigma_2}{\sigma_3}\frac{\Sigma x_1x_3}{N}+r_{13}r_{23}\frac{\sigma_1\sigma_2}{\sigma_3^2}\frac{\Sigma x_3^2}{N}$$
$$=r_{12}\sigma_1\sigma_2-r_{13}\frac{\sigma_1}{\sigma_3}(r_{23}\sigma_2\sigma_3)-r_{23}\frac{\sigma_2}{\sigma_3}(r_{13}\sigma_1\sigma_3)+r_{13}r_{23}\frac{\sigma_1\sigma_2}{\sigma_3^2}(\sigma_3^2)$$
$$=r_{12}\sigma_1\sigma_2-r_{13}r_{23}\sigma_1\sigma_2-r_{23}r_{13}\sigma_1\sigma_2+r_{13}r_{23}\sigma_1\sigma_2$$
$$=\sigma_1\sigma_2r_{12}-\sigma_1\sigma_2r_{13}r_{23}$$
$$=\sigma_1\sigma_2(r_{12}-r_{13}r_{23})$$

8. To show that $\frac{1}{N}\Sigma\left(x_2-r_{23}\frac{\sigma_2}{\sigma_3}x_3\right)\left(x_3-r_{23}\frac{\sigma_3}{\sigma_2}x_2\right)$
$$=\sigma_2\sigma_3r_{23}(r_{23}^2-1)$$

$$\frac{1}{N}\Sigma\left(x_2-r_{23}\frac{\sigma_2}{\sigma_3}x_3\right)\left(x_3-r_{23}\frac{\sigma_3}{\sigma_2}x_2\right)$$
$$=\frac{1}{N}\Sigma\left(x_2x_3-r_{23}\frac{\sigma_2}{\sigma_3}x_3^2-r_{23}\frac{\sigma_3}{\sigma_2}x_2^2+r_{23}^2x_2x_3\right)$$
$$=\frac{\Sigma x_2x_3}{N}-r_{23}\frac{\sigma_2}{\sigma_3}\frac{\Sigma x_3^2}{N}-r_{23}\frac{\sigma_3}{\sigma_2}\frac{\Sigma x_2^2}{N}+r_{23}^2\frac{\Sigma x_2x_3}{N}$$

$$= r_{23}\sigma_2\sigma_3 - r_{23}\frac{\sigma_2}{\sigma_3}(\sigma_3^2) - r_{23}\frac{\sigma_3}{\sigma_2}(\sigma_2^2) + r_{23}^2(r_{23}\sigma_2\sigma_3)$$

$$= r_{23}\sigma_2\sigma_3 - r_{23}\sigma_2\sigma_3 - r_{23}\sigma_2\sigma_3 + r_{23}^3\sigma_2\sigma_3$$

$$= \sigma_2\sigma_3 r_{23}(r_{23}^2 - 1)$$

EXERCISE 32

Show that the following statements are correct.

1. $\dfrac{1}{N}\Sigma x_2\left(x_1 - r_{12}\dfrac{\sigma_1}{\sigma_2}x_2\right) = 0$

2. $\dfrac{1}{N}\Sigma\left(x_2 - r_{12}\dfrac{\sigma_2}{\sigma_1}x_1\right)^2 = \sigma_2^2(1 - r_{12}^2)$

3. $\dfrac{1}{N}\Sigma\left(x_2 - r_{23}\dfrac{\sigma_2}{\sigma_3}x_3\right)^2 = \sigma_2^2(1 - r_{23}^2)$

4. $\dfrac{1}{N}\Sigma x_1(x_1 + x_2 + x_3) = \sigma_1(\sigma_1 + r_{12}\sigma_2 + r_{13}\sigma_3)$

SECOND TEST

1. Factor each of the following expressions into a monomial and a polynomial factor:

    (1) $2x_1^2 + 2x_2^2 + 2x_3^2$

    (2) $cx_1y_1 + cx_2y_2 + cx_3y_3$

    (3) $a_1x + a_2x + a_3x$

    (4) $10pq - 5p + 15p^2$

    (5) $a^2b_1 + a^2b_2 + a^2b_3 + a^2b_4$

    (6) $r_1 - r_1^2$

    (7) $cX_1 + cX_2 + cX_3 + cX_4$

    (8) $M_1a + M_1b + M_1c$

    (9) $\sigma_1^2 - r^2\sigma_1^2 - \sigma_1^2R^2$

    (10) $\sigma_1^2 - \sigma_1^2R_{1.23}^2$

    (11) $\dfrac{x}{a} + \dfrac{y}{a}$

    (12) $pqn_1 + pqn_2 + pqn_3$

2. Assume that x and y represent variables, that all other letters represent constants, and that N is the number of terms to be added in each summation. Place a plus sign in front of each statement which you consider correct and a minus sign in front of each statement which you consider incorrect.

    ———— (1) $\Sigma ax = a\Sigma x$

    ———— (2) $\Sigma xy = x\Sigma y$

——— (3) $\Sigma xy = y\Sigma x$

——— (4) $\Sigma xy = Nxy$

——— (5) $\Sigma c = Nc$

——— (6) $\Sigma ax = x\Sigma a$

——— (7) $\Sigma ax^2 = Nx^2$

——— (8) $\Sigma ax^2 = a\Sigma x^2$

——— (9) $\Sigma 2y = 2\Sigma y$

———(10) $\Sigma(3x)(2y) = 6\Sigma xy$

———(11) $\Sigma x = Nx$

———(12) $\Sigma r\dfrac{\sigma_1}{\sigma_2}xy = r\dfrac{\sigma_1}{\sigma_2}\Sigma xy$

———(13) $\Sigma(x^2 - y^2) = \Sigma x^2 - \Sigma y^2$

———(14) $\Sigma(x - y)^2 = \Sigma x^2 - 2\Sigma xy + \Sigma y^2$

———(15) $\Sigma(x - 1) = \Sigma x - N$

———(16) $\Sigma(y - M) = \Sigma y - NM$

———(17) $\Sigma(y - 3) = Ny - 3N$

———(18) $\Sigma Mx = NMx$

———(19) $\Sigma rx_1^2 = r\Sigma x_1^2$

———(20) $\Sigma axy = x\Sigma ay$

3. In the following problems it is to be understood that x with any subscript whatever, or x without a subscript, represents a variable. Any other letter represents a parameter or constant. The following substitutions may be made:

$$\Sigma x = 0$$
$$\frac{1}{N}\Sigma x_1^2 = \sigma_1^2$$
$$\frac{1}{N}\Sigma x_1 x_2 = r_{12}\sigma_1\sigma_2 = r_{21}\sigma_1\sigma_2$$

Similar substitutions may be made for other subscripts, as for example, $\frac{1}{N}\Sigma x_2 x_3 = r_{23}\sigma_2\sigma_3$. Perform whatever algebraic manipulations and substitutions are necessary, and for each of the following expressions, find an equivalent expression in which the letter x does not appear.

(1) $\dfrac{1}{N}\Sigma(x+a)^2$

(2) $\dfrac{1}{N}\Sigma(x_1+x_2)^2$

(3) $\dfrac{1}{N}\Sigma\left(x_1-r_{12}\dfrac{\sigma_1}{\sigma_2}x_2\right)\left(x_2-r_{12}\dfrac{\sigma_2}{\sigma_1}x_1\right)$

XVII

EXPONENTS

INITIAL TEST

1. Find the numerical value of each of the following:

(1) 4^0 (11) $(4^{-1})^2$ (21) $4^{-1} \div 4^{0.5}$

(2) 4^{-1} (12) $(4^{-1})(4^2)$ (22) $\sqrt[3]{4^6}$

(3) $4^{\frac{1}{2}}$ (13) $(4^{-2})(4^2)$ (23) $\sqrt{4^6}$

(4) $4^{-\frac{1}{2}}$ (14) $4^{-2} \div 4^{-4}$ (24) $\sqrt{4^3}$

(5) $4^{-\frac{3}{2}}$ (15) $4^3 \div 4^{-1}$ (25) $\sqrt{4^{-3}}$

(6) $(4^3)^{\frac{1}{2}}$ (16) $4 \div 4^{-1}$ (26) 3^{-1}

(7) $(-4)^0$ (17) $4^{-1.75} \div 4^{-1.25}$ (27) 1^4

(8) $(-4)^{-1}$ (18) $4^{1.5} \div 4^{-0.5}$ (28) 3^0

(9) $(-4)^{-2}$ (19) $(4^{\frac{1}{2}})^{-2}$ (29) 16^1

(10) $(-4)^{-3}$ (20) $4^{-1.5} \div 4^2$ (30) 16^0

2. Write each answer as 10 with an appropriate exponent.

(1) $10^{4.12} \times 10^{1.75} \div 10^{3.23}$ (4) $\sqrt{\frac{1}{10}}$

(2) $\sqrt{10^{5.16}}$ (5) $\sqrt[5]{10}$

(3) $10^{1.19} \div \sqrt[3]{10^{4.86}}$ (6) $(10^{0.13})^5$

Importance. An understanding of the use of exponents is essential to an understanding of logarithms and their use in computation. The person who intends to study the sections of this book dealing with logarithms and the normal curve should master this present section. It is however possible to study most of the elementary texts in statistical method without needing logarithms, expanding the binomial theorem, or using the mathematical equation of the normal curve. The person who does not intend to study those topics can omit this work on exponents from his study.

Exponent. In previous sections we have used the term *exponent* for a number written at the right and slightly above another number to indicate a power. Thus $a^5 = a \times a \times a \times a \times a$, and 5 is the exponent of a. We have already, for convenience, used $\frac{1}{2}$ as an exponent to indicate square root, but otherwise we have used only positive integers as exponents. Now we will extend that concept to include the use of negative numbers, zero and fractions as exponents.

Laws for Positive Integral Exponents. To make meaningful the laws for working with positive integral exponents, study first the specific exercise in the left hand portion of Table II, and then the symbolic rule at the right, which is in each case a generalization of the specific relationship.

TABLE II

ILLUSTRATIONS OF THE LAWS FOR POSITIVE INTEGRAL EXPONENTS

Specific Relationship	*Generalization*
$a^3 \times a^2 = (aaa)(aa) = a^{3+2} = a^5$ $a^2 \times a^4 = (aa)(aaaa) = a^{2+4} = a^6$	$a^m \times a^n = a^{m+n}$
$a^{10} \div a^3 = \dfrac{aaaaaaaaaa}{aaa} = a^{10-3} = a^7$ $a^5 \div a^2 = \dfrac{aaaaa}{aa} = a^{5-2} = a^3$	$a^m \div a^n = a^{m-n}$
$(a^3)^2 = (aaa)(aaa) = a^{2 \times 3} = a^6$ $(a^2)^5 = (aa)(aa)(aa)(aa)(aa) = a^{10}$	$(a^m)^n = a^{mn}$
$\sqrt{a^{10}}$ = one of the two equal numbers whose product is a^{10}. Now $a^{10} = a^5 \times a^5$. Therefore $\sqrt{a^{10}} = a^{\frac{10}{2}} = a^5$ $\sqrt[4]{a^{20}}$ = one of the four equal factors whose product is a^{20}. Now $a^{20} = (a^5)(a^5)(a^5)(a^5)$. Therefore $\sqrt[4]{a^{20}} = a^{\frac{20}{4}} = a^5$ $\sqrt[3]{a^{21}}$ = one of the three equal factors whose product is a^{21}. Now $a^{21} = (a^7)(a^7)(a^7)$. Therefore $\sqrt[3]{a^{21}} = a^{\frac{21}{3}} = a^7$	$\sqrt[n]{a^m} = a^{\frac{m}{n}}$

Extension of the Laws for Exponents.   We will now assume that these same four laws hold no matter whether m and n are integers or fractions, positive, negative, or zero, and we will consider the meanings which may be attached to fractional and negative exponents in order to make them consistent with these rules.   In Table III is a series of exercises

TABLE III

ILLUSTRATIONS OF THE MEANING OF NEGATIVE, FRACTIONAL, AND ZERO EXPONENTS

Solution by Methods Already Known	Application of the Rules for Exponents	Resulting Definition
$a^2 \div a^3 = \dfrac{aa}{aaa} = \dfrac{1}{a}$	$a^2 \div a^3 = a^{2-3} = a^{-1}$	$a^{-1} = \dfrac{1}{a}$
$a^3 \div a^5 = \dfrac{aaa}{aaaaa} = \dfrac{1}{a^2}$	$a^3 \div a^5 = a^{3-5} = a^{-2}$	$a^{-2} = \dfrac{1}{a^2}$
$3 \div 3^6 = \dfrac{3}{3^6} = \dfrac{1}{3^5}$	$3 \div 3^6 = 3^{1-6} = 3^{-5}$	$3^{-5} = \dfrac{1}{3^5}$
$3^2 \div 3^2 = 9 \div 9 = 1$	$3^2 \div 3^2 = 3^{2-2} = 3^0$	$3^0 = 1$
$16 \div 16 = 1$	$16 \div 16 = 2^4 \div 2^4 = 2^{4-4} = 2^0$	$2^0 = 1$
$12^3 \div 12^3 = 1$	$12^3 \div 12^3 = 12^{3-3} = 12^0$	$12^0 = 1$
One of the 3 equal factors whose product is a is $\sqrt[3]{a}$	$a^{\frac{1}{3}} \cdot a^{\frac{1}{3}} \cdot a^{\frac{1}{3}} = a^{\frac{1}{3}+\frac{1}{3}+\frac{1}{3}} = a$	$a^{\frac{1}{3}} = \sqrt[3]{a}$
One of the 2 equal factors whose product is 5 is $\sqrt{5}$	$5^{\frac{1}{2}} \cdot 5^{\frac{1}{2}} = 5^{\frac{1}{2}+\frac{1}{2}} = 5$	$5^{\frac{1}{2}} = \sqrt{5}$
One of the 7 equal factors whose product is a^4 is $\sqrt[7]{a^4}$	$(a^{\frac{4}{7}})^7 = a^{\frac{28}{7}} = a^4$	$a^{\frac{4}{7}} = \sqrt[7]{a^4}$
$36 \div 216 =$	$6^2 \div 6^3 =$	
$2^5 \div 2^8 =$	$2^5 \div 2^8 =$	
$10^4 \div 10^4 =$		
$7 \div 7^3 =$		
One of the 5 equal factors whose product is 10		
One of the 3 equal factors whose product is 25		
One of the 2 equal factors whose product is 27		

designed to show how such exponents must be defined if these rules are to be made general. The first column shows the solution of an exercise by methods already understood and known to be valid. The second column shows a solution arrived at solely by the application of the four rules. The last column sets these two results equal to each other. Thus the first row of the table suggests that if we define a^{-1} as $\dfrac{1}{a}$, the result of dividing a^2 by a^3 will be consistent whether we get it by applying the rules for exponents or by dividing both terms of a fraction by the same number. Study each of the relationships which is given here in complete form, then fill out the blank portions of the table in similar fashion.

Zero and Negative Exponents. From the foregoing, it appears reasonable to agree that *any finite number raised to the zero power is equal to 1.* At first thought it is surprising that $452^0 = 3^0 = 17^0 = 1296^0$, etc., but on second thought it is apparent that

$$\frac{452}{452} = \frac{3}{3} = \frac{17}{17} = \frac{1296}{1296} = 1.$$

It also appears reasonable to define a^{-m} as equal to $\dfrac{1}{a^m}$. To give still further meaning to these definitions, study the following:

$a^4 = 1 \cdot a \cdot a \cdot a \cdot a$	$2^4 = 16$	$3^4 = 81$
$a^3 = 1 \cdot a \cdot a \cdot a$	$2^3 = 8$	$3^3 = 27$
$a^2 = 1 \cdot a \cdot a$	$2^2 = 4$	$3^2 = 9$
$a^1 = 1 \cdot a$	$2^1 = 2$	$3^1 = 3$
$a^0 = 1$	$2^0 = 1$	$3^0 = 1$
$a^{-1} = 1 \div a$	$2^{-1} = \frac{1}{2}$	$3^{-1} = \frac{1}{3}$
$a^{-2} = 1 \div (a \cdot a)$	$2^{-2} = \frac{1}{4}$	$3^{-2} = \frac{1}{9}$
$a^{-3} = 1 \div (a \cdot a \cdot a)$	$2^{-3} = \frac{1}{8}$	$3^{-3} = \frac{1}{27}$
$a^{-4} = 1 \div (a \cdot a \cdot a \cdot a)$	$2^{-4} = \frac{1}{16}$	$3^{-4} = \frac{1}{81}$

Fractional Exponents. In the same way it is obvious that we can accept $a^{\frac{m}{n}}$ as an alternative way of writing $\sqrt[n]{a^m}$, because this definition is consistent with the outcome of applying the rules for exponents.

EXERCISE 33

1. Write an alternative form equivalent to each of the following:

(1) r^{-3}

(2) $a^{\frac{1}{2}}$

(3) q^0

(4) c^{-4}

(5) $\sqrt[3]{x^2}$

(6) $\left(\dfrac{1}{a}\right)^{-1}$

(7) $\dfrac{1}{x^4}$

(8) $\sqrt{n^5}$

(9) $\dfrac{1}{\sqrt{a}}$

(10) $\dfrac{1}{b^2}$

(11) $\sqrt[4]{a^5}$

(12) $\dfrac{a}{b}$

(13) $\left(\dfrac{1}{c}\right)^{-2}$

(14) $\left(\dfrac{1}{a}\right)^{\frac{1}{2}}$

(15) $\sqrt{x^3}$

(16) $x^{\frac{3}{7}}$

2. In the first column below is a list of exercises. In the second column is the solution which results from substituting immediately such equivalent forms as $\sqrt[n]{a^m}$ for $a^{\frac{m}{n}}$, 1 for a^0, or $\dfrac{1}{a^n}$ for a^{-n}. In the third column is the solution which results from applying the four laws of exponents.

Verify the procedure by ascertaining that the results in column 2 are equivalent to those in column 3.

Exercise	Substitution of Equivalent Forms	Application of Laws
$a^{-3} \div a^{-5}$	$\dfrac{1}{a^3} \div \dfrac{1}{a^5} = \dfrac{a^5}{a^3} = a^2$	$a^{-3-(-5)} = a^{-3+5} = a^2$
$x^{-5} \cdot x^2 \cdot x^3$	$\dfrac{x^2 \cdot x^3}{x^5} = 1$	$x^{-5+2+3} = x^0$
$(4^{\frac{1}{2}})^6$	$2^6 = 64$	$4^{\frac{6}{2}} = 4^3$
$(25^{-2})^{\frac{1}{4}}$	$\sqrt[4]{\frac{1}{625}} = \frac{1}{5}$	$25^{-\frac{2}{4}} = 25^{-\frac{1}{2}} = \frac{1}{5}$
$(8^2)^{\frac{1}{3}}$	$64^{\frac{1}{3}} = \sqrt[3]{64} = 4$	$8^{\frac{2}{3}} = 2^2 = 4$
$a^2 \div a^{-1}$	$a^2 \div \dfrac{1}{a} = a^2 \cdot a = a^3$	$a^{2-(-1)} = a^3$

3. Find the numerical values of the expressions shown below

Example 1.　　$25^{-\frac{3}{2}} = \dfrac{1}{25^{\frac{3}{2}}} = \dfrac{1}{(5)^3} = \dfrac{1}{125}$

Example 2.　　$\left(\dfrac{1}{8}\right)^{-\frac{2}{3}} = \dfrac{1}{\left(\frac{1}{8}\right)^{\frac{2}{3}}} = 8^{\frac{2}{3}} = (8^{\frac{1}{3}})^2 = 2^2 = 4$

(1) $64^{\frac{2}{3}}$　　　　　　(6) $25^{-\frac{1}{2}}$　　　　　　(11) $49^{\frac{1}{2}}$

(2) $400^{\frac{1}{2}}$　　　　　(7) $(\frac{1}{3})^{-2}$　　　　　(12) $125^{\frac{2}{3}}$

(3) $400^{-\frac{1}{2}}$　　　　(8) $(\frac{1}{4})^{-2}$　　　　　(13) $(\frac{1}{8})^{-\frac{1}{3}}$

(4) 75^0　　　　　　　(9) $(\frac{1}{2})^{-3}$　　　　　(14) $(5^{-1})^2$

(5) $27^{\frac{1}{3}}$　　　　　　(10) $(\frac{1}{36})^{-\frac{1}{2}}$　　　(15) $(3^{-2})^{\frac{1}{2}}$

4. Write the answers to the following exercises as 10 with the appropriate exponent.

Example 1.　$\sqrt{10^{3.14}} = 10^{1.57}$

Example 2.　$\dfrac{10^{3.48}}{10^{4.12}} = 10^{-0.64}$

Example 3.　$(10^{2.14})^{-1.3} =$
　　　　　$10^{-(2.14)(1.3)} = 10^{-2.782}$

(1) $(10^{0.42})^3$　　　　　　　(9) $\sqrt[3]{10}$

(2) $\sqrt{10^{0.28}}$　　　　　　　(10) $\sqrt[4]{10}$

(3) $10^{1.36} \times 10^{2.49} \div 10^{1.02}$　　(11) $\sqrt[8]{10}$

(4) $\sqrt[3]{10^{4.14}} \div 10^{5.09}$　　　(12) $\sqrt{\frac{1}{10}}$

(5) $(10^{1.29})^2 \div (10^{0.67})^3$　　(13) $\sqrt[3]{\frac{1}{10}}$

(6) $(10^{1.49})^{1.2}$　　　　　(14) $\sqrt[4]{\frac{1}{10}}$

(7) $10^{2.43} \div \sqrt[3]{10^{6.03}}$　　　(15) $\sqrt[4]{10^3}$

(8) $\sqrt{10^3}$

5. Find the numerical values of the expressions shown below.

Caution: In the chapter on Signed Numbers we learned that odd powers of negative numbers are negative, even powers of negative numbers are positive. Consequently a negative number raised to powers of -1, -3, -5, -7, etc., will be negative, and a negative number raised to powers of -2, -4, -6, -8, etc., will be positive.

(1) $(-2)^{-1}$　　　　　(4) $(-8)^{\frac{1}{3}}$　　　　　(7) $(-3)^{-4}$

(2) $(-4)^{-2}$　　　　　(5) $(-1)^{-1}$　　　　　(8) $(-3)^{-3}$

(3) $(-1)^2$　　　　　　(6) $(-6)^{-2}$　　　　　(9) $(-8)^{-\frac{1}{3}}$

SECOND TEST

1. Find the numerical value of each of the following:

(1) 9^0	(11) $\sqrt[3]{9^6}$	(21) $(9^3)^{\frac{1}{2}}$
(2) $9^{\frac{1}{2}}$	(12) $\sqrt{9^3}$	(22) $(-9)^{-1}$
(3) $9^{-\frac{3}{2}}$	(13) 1^3	(23) $(-9)^{-2}$
(4) $(-9)^0$	(14) 5^0	(24) $(\frac{1}{9})^{-2}$
(5) $(-9)^{-3}$	(15) $\sqrt{9^{-3}}$	(25) $(9^{-1})^2$
(6) $(9^{-1})(9^2)$	(16) $64^{\frac{1}{2}}$	(26) $(9^{-2})(9^2)$
(7) $9^{-2} \div 9^{-4}$	(17) 2^{-1}	(27) $3^3 \div 3^{-1}$
(8) $9 \div 9^{-1}$	(18) $\sqrt[4]{9^5}$	(28) $9^{-1.75} \div 9^{-1.25}$
(9) $9^{-1.5} \div 9$	(19) 9^{-1}	(29) $(9^1)^{-2}$
(10) $9^{2.5} \div 9^{0.5}$	(20) $9^{-\frac{1}{2}}$	(30) $9^{-1} \div 9^{0.5}$

2. Write each answer as 10 with the appropriate exponent.

(1) $10^{3.95} \times 10^{2.17} \div 10^{4.28}$ (4) $\sqrt[3]{\frac{1}{10}}$

(2) $\sqrt{10^{3.02}}$ (5) $\sqrt[8]{10}$

(3) $10^{0.05} \div \sqrt{10^{2.04}}$ (6) $(10^{0.17})^{-2}$

XVIII

LOGARITHMS

INITIAL TEST

The table of mantissas on pages 174 and 175 is to be used for the following computations.

1. $\sqrt[3]{4362}$

2. $\dfrac{685 \times 473}{(321)^2}$

3. $(1.072)^6$

4. $0.029 \div 1.354$

5. $\sqrt{14.35 \div 372.6}$

6. Find the geometric mean of 2.41, 2.68, 2.39, 2.12, and 2.53.

Importance. A statistical computer who has access to computing machines and computing tables is not likely to make extensive use of logarithms, and if one had to choose between learning to operate a machine and learning to use a table of logarithms, the former would doubtless be more valuable. A great advantage of machine computation is that it can be used for all operations, whereas logarithms can be used only in multiplication, division, and the extraction of roots. However logarithms are of interest to the statistician in several ways besides that of being an aid in routine calculations. They are the basis for the slide rule, for logarithmic graph paper, and for various alignment charts used in graphic computation. Their use in connection with computing the geometric mean and in plotting the "normal curve of error" is important for the statistician.

This section may be omitted by those who want only the minimum of work necessary for the most elementary courses in statistics.

168

Computing by Means of a Table of Powers. The adjacent table of powers of the number 2 can be used to facilitate certain computations. For example,

$$512 \times 256 = 2^9 \times 2^8 = 2^{17} = 131072$$

$$\sqrt{262144} = \sqrt{2^{18}} = 2^9 = 512$$

$$(0.0078125)(16384) =$$

$$(2^{-7})(2^{14}) = 2^7 = 128$$

$$2048 \div (0.03125) =$$

$$2^{11} \div 2^{-5} = 2^{16} = 65536$$

$$(32)^3 = (2^5)^3 = 2^{15} = 32768$$

Logarithm of a Number. In the statement $2^{11} = 2048$, we say that 11 is the exponent of 2 or that 11 is the logarithm of 2048 to the base 2. This statement is written

$$\log_2 2048 = 11.$$

Obviously a logarithm is an exponent.

Read in words, and verify from the table:

$$\log_2 65536 = 16$$
$$\log_2 0.015625 = -6$$
$$\log_2 1 = 0$$
$$\log_2 131072 = 17$$
$$\log_2 128 = 7$$

TABLE IV

POWERS OF 2

2^{20}	$=$	1048576
2^{19}	$=$	524288
2^{18}	$=$	262144
2^{17}	$=$	131072
2^{16}	$=$	65536
2^{15}	$=$	32768
2^{14}	$=$	16384
2^{13}	$=$	8192
2^{12}	$=$	4096
2^{11}	$=$	2048
2^{10}	$=$	1024
2^9	$=$	512
2^8	$=$	256
2^7	$=$	128
2^6	$=$	64
2^5	$=$	32
2^4	$=$	16
2^3	$=$	8
2^2	$=$	4
2^1	$=$	2
2^0	$=$	1
2^{-1}	$=$	0.5
2^{-2}	$=$	0.25
2^{-3}	$=$	0.125
2^{-4}	$=$	0.0625
2^{-5}	$=$	0.03125
2^{-6}	$=$	0.015625
2^{-7}	$=$	0.0078125
2^{-8}	$=$	0.00390625
2^{-9}	$=$	0.001953125
2^{-10}	$=$	0.0009765625

EXERCISE 34

1. (1) $\log_2 256 =$ (3) $\log_2 0.0625 =$
  (2) $\log_2 0.25 =$ (4) $\log_2 0.0078125 =$

2. Read answers from the table of powers of 2.

  (1) $1048576 \div 65536 =$

  (2) $4096 \div 0.03125 =$

  (3) $\sqrt[3]{262144} =$

(4) $(16)^4 =$

(5) $\dfrac{(0.0625)(32768)(0.00390625)}{256} =$

(6) $(512)^2 =$

(7) $\sqrt{0.015625} =$

(8) $\sqrt[3]{0.015625} =$

3. Fill the blank spaces with appropriate words.

(1) In multiplying two numbers with the same base, we ————— their logarithms.

(2) In dividing one number by a second number with the same base, we ————— the logarithm of the second number ————— the logarithm of the first

(3) In taking the cube root of a number we ————— its logarithm ————— —————.

(4) In taking the fifth root of a number we ————— its logarithm ————— —————.

(5) In squaring a number we ————— its logarithm ————— —————.

(6) In raising a number to the nth power, we ————— its logarithm ————— —————.

(7) In taking the nth root of a number, we ————— its logarithm ————— —————.

Table of Powers of Ten. It is evident that tables of logarithms of numbers can be made up for any base, just as Table IV on page 169 was made for the base 2. However, since our number system has the base 10, multiplication and division by powers of 10 are particularly easy, and therefore it is more convenient to use a table of logarithms with the base 10 for ordinary computations. We will now make up a small table of powers of 10 from which we can discover the general plan of computation with logarithms.

The values inserted in Table V may be found thus:

$$10^{0.5} = \sqrt{10} = 3.162$$
$$10^{0.25} = \sqrt{10^{0.5}} = \sqrt{3.162} = 1.778$$
$$10^{0.125} = \sqrt{10^{0.25}} = \sqrt{1.778} = 1.333$$

ll other values in Table V can be found from these, for example:

$$10^{0.75} = (10^{0.5})(10^{0.25}) = 5.623$$
$$10^{0.375} = \sqrt{10^{0.75}} = \sqrt{5.623} = 2.371$$
$$10^{0.875} = \sqrt{10^{1.75}} = \sqrt{56.23} = 7.499$$

TABLE V
POWERS OF 10

$10^{0.000} = 1.000$	$10^{1.000} = 10.00$	$10^{2.000} = 100.0$	$10^{3.000} = 1000$
$10^{0.125} = 1.333$	$10^{1.125} = 13.33$	$10^{2.125} = 133.3$	$10^{3.125} = 1333$
$10^{0.250} = 1.778$	$10^{1.250} = 17.78$	$10^{2.250} = 177.8$	$10^{3.250} = 1778$
$10^{0.375} = 2.371$	$10^{1.375} = 23.71$	$10^{2.375} = 237.1$	$10^{3.375} = 2371$
$10^{0.500} = 3.162$	$10^{1.500} = 31.62$	$10^{2.500} = 316.2$	$10^{3.500} = 3162$
$10^{0.625} = 4.217$	$10^{1.625} = 42.17$	$10^{2.625} = 421.7$	$10^{3.625} = 4217$
$10^{0.750} = 5.623$	$10^{1.750} = 56.23$	$10^{2.750} = 562.3$	$10^{3.750} = 5623$
$10^{0.875} = 7.499$	$10^{1.875} = 74.99$	$10^{2.875} = 749.9$	$10^{3.875} = 7499$

EXERCISE 35

By aid of the table of powers of 10, perform the following operations:

. 1.333×316.2

. $3.162 \times 17.78 \times 4.217$

. $(2.371)^5$

. $\sqrt[3]{5623}$

. $\dfrac{2371 \times 13.33}{421.7}$

6. $(56.23)^3 \div (23.71)^2$

7. $\sqrt[5]{1333}$

8. $\dfrac{7.499 \times 177.8}{(2.371)^2}$

9. $5.623 \div \sqrt{31.62}$

10. $\sqrt{1778} \div \sqrt{316.2}$

Writing a Number in "Standard Form". Any number may be considered to be the product of some integral power of ten, either positive or negative, and a number whose value is between 1 and 10. This form is particularly useful in astronomy, where large numbers are used. Thus

$$623 = 6.23(10^2)$$
$$4100 = 4.1(10^3)$$
$$0.00017 = 1.7(10^{-4})$$
$$65100000 = 6.51(10^7)$$
$$0.3692 = 3.692(10^{-1})$$

Mantissa and Characteristic. From the table of power
of 10, we see that each logarithm is made up of two parts
an integer and a decimal fraction. The integer is called th
characteristic of the logarithm, the decimal fraction is calle
the *mantissa*. Notice that all the logarithms in any one hori
zontal row of Table V have the same mantissa. In wha
way are the corresponding numbers alike? Notice that al
the logarithms in any one vertical column have the sam
characteristic. In what way are the numbers in one colum
alike?

It is obvious that the characteristic determines the positio
of the decimal point and has nothing to do with the sequenc
of digits, while the mantissa determines the sequence o
digits and has nothing to do with the position of the decima
point. We may write down the figures in one horizontal row
extending the series in both directions, thus:

$$10^{6.750} = 5623000$$
$$10^{5.750} = 562300$$
$$10^{4.750} = 56230$$
$$10^{3.750} = 5623$$
$$10^{2.750} = 562.3$$
$$10^{1.750} = 56.23$$
$$10^{0.750} = 5.623$$
$$10^{0.750-1} = 0.5623$$
$$10^{0.750-2} = 0.05623$$
$$10^{0.750-3} = 0.005623$$
$$10^{0.750-4} = 0.0005623$$

Rules for Size of Characteristic. The preceding table sug
gests these rules:

When a number is larger than 1, its characteristic is on
less than the number of digits to the left of the decima
point in the number. When a number is smaller than 1, it
characteristic is negative and is numerically one more tha

the number of zeros between the decimal point and the first significant digit in the number.

Since the negative sign applies to the characteristic only, and not to the mantissa, it is usually written directly over the characteristic, thus:

$$\text{Log } 0.05623 \quad = \bar{2}.750$$
$$\text{Log } 0.00005623 = \bar{5}.750$$

Exercise 36

1. What is the characteristic of the logarithm of each of these numbers?

(1) 5327	(6) 12.06	(11) 0.0037
(2) 490.16	(7) 3.09	(12) 0.34
(3) 0.000013	(8) 1.03	(13) 0.00004
(4) 5.1002	(9) 9.16	(14) 4.0003
(5) 62139.4	(10) 91.6	(15) 51.31

2. Rewrite each of the numbers in the preceding exercise in "standard form".

3. What is the relationship between the characteristics of the logarithms of these numbers as found in Exercise 1 and the exponents of 10 as found in Exercise 2?

Table of Mantissas. Since the characteristics of the logarithms of numbers can be found by inspection, the tables need furnish only the mantissas and the sequence of digits in the corresponding numbers. Such a table is found on pages 174 and 175. Here the mantissas are in the body of the table, and the numbers are in the margins. To find the mantissa of the logarithm of 426 we look for 42 in the left hand vertical column headed N and for 6 in the horizontal row across the top of the table. The mantissa we seek is in the cell of the table corresponding to these two entries, that is it is in the column headed 6 and in the row to the right of 42. This mantissa is 6294. Therefore $\log_{10} 426 = 2.6294$, or $10^{2.6294} = 426$.

TABLE VI

MANTISSAS

N	0	1	2	3	4	5	6	7	8	9
10	0000	0043	0086	0128	0170	0212	0253	0294	0334	0374
11	0414	0453	0492	0531	0569	0607	0645	0682	0719	0755
12	0792	0828	0864	0899	0934	0969	1004	1038	1072	1106
13	1139	1173	1206	1239	1271	1303	1335	1367	1399	1430
14	1461	1492	1523	1553	1584	1614	1644	1673	1703	1732
15	1761	1790	1818	1847	1875	1903	1931	1959	1987	2014
16	2041	2068	2095	2122	2148	2175	2201	2227	2253	2279
17	2304	2330	2355	2380	2405	2430	2455	2480	2504	2529
18	2553	2577	2601	2625	2648	2672	2695	2718	2742	2765
19	2788	2810	2833	2856	2878	2900	2923	2945	2967	2989
20	3010	3032	3054	3075	3096	3118	3139	3160	3181	3201
21	3222	3243	3263	3284	3304	3324	3345	3365	3385	3404
22	3424	3444	3464	3483	3502	3522	3541	3560	3579	3598
23	3617	3636	3655	3674	3692	3711	3729	3747	3766	3784
24	3802	3820	3838	3856	3874	3892	3909	3927	3945	3962
25	3979	3997	4014	4031	4048	4065	4082	4099	4116	4133
26	4150	4166	4183	4200	4216	4232	4249	4265	4281	4298
27	4314	4330	4346	4362	4378	4393	4409	4425	4440	4456
28	4472	4487	4502	4518	4533	4548	4564	4579	4594	4609
29	4624	4639	4654	4669	4683	4698	4713	4728	4742	4757
30	4771	4786	4800	4814	4829	4843	4857	4871	4886	4900
31	4914	4928	4942	4955	4969	4983	4997	5011	5024	5038
32	5051	5065	5079	5092	5105	5119	5132	5145	5159	5172
33	5185	5198	5211	5224	5237	5250	5263	5276	5289	5302
34	5315	5328	5340	5353	5366	5378	5391	5403	5416	5428
35	5441	5453	5465	5478	5490	5502	5514	5527	5539	5551
36	5563	5575	5587	5599	5611	5623	5635	5647	5658	5670
37	5682	5694	5705	5717	5729	5740	5752	5763	5775	5786
38	5798	5809	5821	5832	5843	5855	5866	5877	5888	5899
39	5911	5922	5933	5944	5955	5966	5977	5988	5999	6010
40	6021	6031	6042	6053	6064	6075	6085	6096	6107	6117
41	6128	6138	6149	6160	6170	6180	6191	6201	6212	6222
42	6232	6243	6253	6263	6274	6284	6294	6304	6314	6325
43	6335	6345	6355	6365	6375	6385	6395	6405	6415	6425
44	6435	6444	6454	6464	6474	6484	6493	6503	6513	6522
45	6532	6542	6551	6561	6571	6580	6590	6599	6609	6618
46	6628	6637	6646	6656	6665	6675	6684	6693	6702	6712
47	6721	6730	6739	6749	6758	6767	6776	6785	6794	6803
48	6812	6821	6830	6839	6848	6857	6866	6875	6884	6893
49	6902	6911	6920	6928	6937	6946	6955	6964	6972	6981
50	6990	6998	7007	7016	7024	7033	7042	7050	7059	7067
51	7076	7084	7093	7101	7110	7118	7126	7135	7143	7152
52	7160	7168	7177	7185	7193	7202	7210	7218	7226	7235
53	7243	7251	7259	7267	7275	7284	7292	7300	7308	7316
54	7324	7332	7340	7348	7356	7364	7372	7380	7388	7396

TABLE VI (*Continued*)

MANTISSAS

N	0	1	2	3	4	5	6	7	8	9
55	7404	7412	7419	7427	7435	7443	7451	7459	7466	7474
56	7482	7490	7497	7505	7513	7520	7528	7536	7543	7551
57	7559	7566	7574	7582	7589	7597	7604	7612	7619	7627
58	7634	7642	7649	7657	7664	7672	7679	7686	7694	7701
59	7709	7716	7723	7731	7738	7745	7752	7760	7767	7774
60	7782	7789	7796	7803	7810	7818	7825	7832	7839	7846
61	7853	7860	7868	7875	7882	7889	7896	7903	7910	7917
62	7924	7931	7938	7945	7952	7959	7966	7973	7980	7987
63	7993	8000	8007	8014	8021	8028	8035	8041	8048	8055
64	8062	8069	8075	8082	8089	8096	8102	8109	8116	8122
65	8129	8136	8142	8149	8156	8162	8169	8176	8182	8189
66	8195	8202	8209	8215	8222	8228	8235	8241	8248	8254
67	8261	8267	8274	8280	8287	8293	8299	8306	8312	8319
68	8325	8331	8338	8344	8351	8357	8363	8370	8376	8382
69	8388	8395	8401	8407	8414	8420	8426	8432	8439	8445
70	8451	8457	8463	8470	8476	8482	8488	8494	8500	8506
71	8513	8519	8525	8531	8537	8543	8549	8555	8561	8567
72	8573	8579	8585	8591	8597	8603	8609	8615	8621	8627
73	8633	8639	8645	8651	8657	8663	8669	8675	8681	8686
74	8692	8698	8704	8710	8716	8722	8727	8733	8739	8745
75	8751	8756	8762	8768	8774	8779	8785	8791	8797	8802
76	8808	8814	8820	8825	8831	8837	8842	8848	8854	8859
77	8865	8871	8876	8882	8887	8893	8899	8904	8910	8915
78	8921	8927	8932	8938	8943	8949	8954	8960	8965	8971
79	8976	8982	8987	8993	8998	9004	9009	9015	9020	9025
80	9031	9036	9042	9047	9053	9058	9063	9069	9074	9079
81	9085	9090	9096	9101	9106	9112	9117	9122	9128	9133
82	9138	9143	9149	9154	9159	9165	9170	9175	9180	9186
83	9191	9196	9201	9206	9212	9217	9222	9227	9232	9238
84	9243	9248	9253	9258	9263	9269	9274	9279	9284	9289
85	9294	9299	9304	9309	9315	9320	9325	9330	9335	9340
86	9345	9350	9355	9360	9365	9370	9375	9380	9385	9390
87	9395	9400	9405	9410	9415	9420	9425	9430	9435	9440
88	9445	9450	9455	9460	9465	9469	9474	9479	9484	9489
89	9494	9499	9504	9509	9513	9518	9523	9528	9533	9538
90	9542	9547	9552	9557	9562	9566	9571	9576	9581	9586
91	9590	9595	9600	9605	9609	9614	9619	9624	9628	9633
92	9638	9643	9647	9652	9657	9661	9666	9671	9675	9680
93	9685	9689	9694	9699	9703	9708	9713	9717	9722	9727
94	9731	9736	9741	9745	9750	9754	9759	9763	9768	9773
95	9777	9782	9786	9791	9795	9800	9805	9809	9814	9818
96	9823	9827	9832	9836	9841	9845	9850	9854	9859	9863
97	9868	9872	9877	9881	9886	9890	9894	9899	9903	9908
98	9912	9917	9921	9926	9930	9934	9939	9943	9948	9952
99	9956	9961	9965	9969	9974	9978	9983	9987	9991	9996

EXERCISE 37

1. Verify the following from the table of mantissas:

(1) $\log_{10} 62.9 = 1.7987$ (5) $3.9299 = \log_{10} 8510$

(2) $\log_{10} 0.531 = \overline{1}.7251$ (6) $0.9974 = \log_{10} 9.94$

(3) $\log_{10} 1300 = 3.1139$ (7) $\overline{1}.9101 = \log_{10} 0.813$

(4) $\log_{10} 70500 = 4.8482$ (8) $\overline{2}.2095 = \log_{10} 0.0162$

2. What is the logarithm of

(1) 193   (4) 1.09   (7) 25.7

(2) 25000   (5) 0.004   (8) 3.68

(3) 0.016   (6) 20000   (9) 13.7

3. What is the number whose logarithm is

(1) 0.6902   (4) $\overline{3}.6010$ (7) 1.9671

(2) 3.7388   (5) 0.8463   (8) 2.8388

(3) 1.1847   (6) $\overline{1}.7427$ (9) $\overline{2}.7474$

Interpolation. The table of mantissas on pages 174 and 175 gives the logarithm of every three-place number, and by linear interpolation we may find the logarithms of four-place numbers to a very fair degree of accuracy. Linear interpolation is discussed on pages 28 to 30.

Example 1. Find the logarithm of 9563.

Mantissa of $956 = 9805$

" " $957 = \underline{9809}$

$4 = \Delta$

Mantissa of $9563 = 9805 + (.3)(4) = 9806.2$

Therefore $\log_{10} 9563 = 3.9806$, dropping digits beyond the fourth decimal place in the mantissa.

Example 2. What is the number whose logarithm is $\overline{2}.8908$?

$$6\left[\ 4\left[\begin{array}{l}8904 = \text{mantissa of } 777\\8908 = \ \text{``}\ \ \text{``}\ \ ?\end{array}\right.\right.\\ \qquad 8910 = \ \ \text{``}\ \ \text{``}\ \ 778$$

Since the given mantissa is $\frac{4}{6}$ of the way from 8904 to 8910, the required number must be approximately $\frac{4}{6}$ of the way from 777 to 778, or 777.667. Since the characteristic is -2, the number sought must be 0.07777, rounding off the result to four significant figures.

Caution. Linear interpolation gives us only an approximation to the correct value, and therefore it would not be permissible to write results with a false appearance of accuracy. *The number may be carried to one more place only. No additional places should be added to the mantissa.*

EXERCISE 38

1. Find the logarithms of

(1) 8905	(4) 721300	(7) 3.792
(2) 12.37	(5) 0.01146	(8) 4.681
(3) 4.003	(6) 0.2354	(9) 173.4

2. Find the numbers whose logarithms are

(1) 3.6254	(3) $\bar{1}.8214$	(5) 0.1422
(2) 1.0391	(4) $\bar{2}.6214$	(6) 1.3618

Computation by Means of Logarithms. The rules for computation with logarithms have been suggested in Question **3** of Exercise 34, and also in the rules for operations with exponents given in the preceding chapter. The rules for logarithmic computation are of course exactly the same as the rules for exponents. They will now be stated again in schematic form.

Computation with Numbers	Computation with Logarithms
$A \times B$	$\log A + \log B$
$A \div B$	$\log A - \log B$
A^n	$n \log A$
$\sqrt[n]{A}$	$\dfrac{1}{n} \log A$

The following illustrations have been chosen to call attention to certain points on which errors are sometimes made by the novice.

Example 1. $6.803 \times 0.04362 \times 0.512 = ?$

$$\begin{aligned}
\log 6.803 &= 0.8327 \\
\log 0.04362 &= \overline{2}.6397 \\
\log 0.512 &= \overline{1}.7093 \\
\log \text{ product} &= \overline{\overline{1}}.1817
\end{aligned}$$

$$\text{Product} = 0.1520$$

Example 2. $\sqrt[3]{0.1325} = ?$

$$\log 0.1325 = \overline{1}.1222$$

To take the cube root of a number we divide its logarithm by 3, but if we divide $\overline{1}.1222$ by 3 we shall have an awkward result. Consequently, we first change the log to $2.1222 - 3$, so that when we divide by 3 the result will be $0.7074 - 1$ or $\overline{1}.7074$. The number whose logarithm is $\overline{1}.7074$ is 0.5098, which is $\sqrt[3]{0.1325}$.

Geometric Mean. The geometric mean of n numbers is the nth root of their product. This has certain important uses in computing mean rate of change in studies of prices, rate of growth, and the like. Logarithms are indispensable in computing the geometric mean.

Example. Find the geometric mean of 112, 107, 119, 102, 109.

$$\text{Geometric mean} = (112 \cdot 107 \cdot 119 \cdot 102 \cdot 109)^{\frac{1}{5}}$$

$$\begin{aligned}
\log 112 &= 2.0492 \\
\log 107 &= 2.0294 \\
\log 119 &= 2.0755 \\
\log 102 &= 2.0086 \\
\log 109 &= 2.0374
\end{aligned}$$

log of product = 10.2001

$\frac{1}{5}$log of product = 2.0400

Geometric mean = 109.6

EXERCISE 39

Perform the following computations by means of the table of mantissas on pages 174 and 175.

1. $(21.03)^{\frac{1}{4}}$

2. $\dfrac{37.62 \times 4.921}{682.3}$

3. $\sqrt[3]{7923}$

4. $(0.0412)^2$

5. $\{0.682\}^{\frac{1}{2}}$

6. $\dfrac{52.34}{(0.631)^2}$

7. Find the geometric mean of 54, 59, 51, 46, 62, 49, 57.

8. Find the geometric mean of 0.123, 0.468, 0.097, 0.322.

9. $(68.19)^{\frac{1}{6}}$

10. $\left\{ \dfrac{9.723 \times 8.46}{0.041} \right\}^{\frac{1}{2}}$

SECOND TEST

Perform the following computations by means of the table of mantissas on pages 174 and 175.

1. $\sqrt[5]{2.681}$

2. $\dfrac{(725)(6304)}{(462)^2}$

3. $(0.0312)^3$

4. $0.0693 \div 2.144$

5. $\sqrt{\dfrac{(32.16)(1.423)}{79.47}}$

6. Find the geometric mean of 1.02, 0.98, 0.96, 1.07, 1.09, 1.01.

XIX

SYMMETRY AND HOMOGENEITY OF ALGEBRAIC EXPRESSIONS

INITIAL TEST

1. Place a check mark in front of each homogeneous expression.

—— (1) $x^2 - 2xy + y^2$

—— (2) $x^3 - 3x^2 + 3x$

—— (3) $x^4 - 4x^2y^2 + xy^5 + 2$

—— (4) $x^7 + x^3y^4$

—— (5) $x^4 - x^2 + 1$

—— (6) $\Sigma x^4 + (\Sigma x^2)^2$

—— (7) $\mu_6 - \mu_3^2$ where $\mu_6 = \dfrac{\Sigma x^6}{N}$ and $\mu_3 = \dfrac{\Sigma x^3}{N}$

—— (8) $\mu_6 - \mu_4^2$ where $\mu_6 = \dfrac{\Sigma x^6}{N}$ and $\mu_4 = \dfrac{\Sigma x^4}{N}$

—— (9) $\mu_8 - \mu_4^2$ where $\mu_8 = \dfrac{\Sigma x^8}{N}$ and $\mu_4 = \dfrac{\Sigma x^4}{N}$

——(10) $\mu_{2a} - \mu_a^2$ where $\mu_{2a} = \dfrac{\Sigma x^{2a}}{N}$ and $\mu_a = \dfrac{\Sigma x^a}{N}$

2. Place a check mark in front of each expression symmetrical with respect to x and y.

——(1) $x^2 - 2xy + y^2$

——(2) $x + 3y$

——(3) $x^4 + 3xy + y^4 + 10$

——(4) $x^2 - y^2$

——(5) $\dfrac{3}{x} + \dfrac{3}{y}$

——(6) $\Sigma xy - (\Sigma x)(\Sigma y)$

——(7) $\dfrac{\sigma_{x+y} - \sigma_x - \sigma_y}{2\sigma_x \sigma_y}$

——(8) $r_{xw} - r_{xy}r_{yw}$

——(9) $\sigma_x^2 - 2r\sigma_x\sigma_y + \sigma_y^2$

3. A familiar statistical formula is

$$\sigma_{1.234} = \sigma_1 \sqrt{1 - r_{12}^2} \sqrt{1 - r_{13.2}^2} \sqrt{1 - r_{14.23}^2}$$

Do not try to understand this formula, but using it as a model write the formula for $\sigma_{2.345}$.

4. Consider that r_{12} and σ_1 are of zero order,

$r_{12.3}$ and $\sigma_{1.2}$ are of first order,

$r_{12.34}$ and $\sigma_{1.23}$ are of second order,

$r_{12.345}$ and $\sigma_{1.234}$ are of third order, and so on.

Place a check mark in front of each expression in which the r's and σ's are of the same order.

____(1) $r_{45.123} \dfrac{\sigma_{4.1235}}{\sigma_{5.1234}}$

____(3) $\sigma_2^2(1-r_{25}^2)(1-r_{24.5}^2)(1-r_{23.45}^2)$

____(2) $r_{24.31} \dfrac{\sigma_{2.31}}{\sigma_{4.31}}$

____(4) $\dfrac{r_{46.21}-r_{47.21}r_{67.21}}{\sqrt{1-r_{47.21}^2}\sqrt{1-r_{67.21}^2}}$

5. There are three variables designated as x_4, x_5, and x_6. The formula $\dfrac{r_{46}-r_{45}r_{65}}{\sqrt{1-r_{45}^2}\sqrt{1-r_{65}^2}}$ is the formula for the correlation between two of them when the influence of the third is eliminated. Without trying to understand what the formula means, decide which of the variables is unique. Which of the r's is unique.

6. The formula $\dfrac{r_{14.2}-r_{13.2}r_{43.2}}{\sqrt{1-r_{13.2}^2}\sqrt{1-r_{43.2}^2}}$ relates to the variables x_1, x_2, x_3, and x_4. Which two are treated symmetrically?

Importance. While texts in elementary statistics do not use the terms symmetry and homogeneity, the concepts underlying them are helpful in studying correlation, particularly partial correlation, and in studying what statisticians call the higher moments. The person who omits this section will probably never be aware of needing its help. The person who masters these easy concepts will enjoy a fuller comprehension of many statistical formulas. This material is not needed at the beginning of a course in statistical method and may well be postponed until correlation is to be studied.

Symmetry. When two variables enter into an expression on the same basis the expression is said to be symmetrical with respect to them. In such an expression, the two variables can be interchanged without affecting the expression. In the expression $x^2 - 4xy + y^2$, if we put x in place of y, and y in place of x we have $y^2 - 4yx + x^2$ which is exactly like the original except for order. We know that the order of factors does not affect a product and the order of addends does not affect a sum. Hence $x^2 - 4xy + y^2$ remains the same when x and y are interchanged, and is therefore symmetrical with respect to them.

A familiar statistical formula is $r_{xy} = \dfrac{\Sigma xy}{N \sigma_x \sigma_y}$. If we interchange x and y this becomes $r_{yx} = \dfrac{\Sigma yx}{N \sigma_y \sigma_x}$.

Now $xy = yx$ and therefore $\Sigma xy = \Sigma yx$. Consequently the right hand members of the two expressions are identical and therefore we must agree that $r_{xy} = r_{yx}$. Thus we say that r_{xy} is a symmetrical function of x and y.

Consider the expression $r_{xz.y} = \dfrac{r_{xz} - r_{xy} r_{zy}}{\sqrt{1 - r^2_{xy}} \sqrt{1 - r^2_{zy}}}$. If we interchange x and y here we have $r_{yz.x} = \dfrac{r_{yz} - r_{yx} r_{zx}}{\sqrt{1 - r^2_{yx}} \sqrt{1 - r^2_{zx}}}$. It is apparent that the right hand members of the two expressions are not the same, and we must conclude that $r_{xz.y}$ and $r_{yz.x}$ have different meanings (whatever those meanings may be) and that neither of them is a symmetrical function of x and y. If however we interchange x and z, we have $r_{zx.y} = \dfrac{r_{zx} - r_{zy} r_{xy}}{\sqrt{1 - r^2_{zy}} \sqrt{1 - r^2_{xy}}}$. If we apply the statement in the previous paragraph that $r_{xy} = r_{yx}$, we would conclude that $r_{zx} = r_{xz}$, and that therefore an interchange of z and x in the formula leaves it the same as before. If we try to interchange z and y we will find the outcome somewhat similar to that of interchanging x and y. It thus appears that the expression $r_{xz.y} = \dfrac{r_{xz} - r_{xy} r_{zy}}{\sqrt{1 - r^2_{xy}} \sqrt{1 - r^2_{zy}}}$ is symmetrical with respect to x and z and that y is a *unique* variable. If instead of centering our attention upon the variables x, y, and z, we look at the r's, we will see that r_{xy} and r_{zy} are treated in exactly the same fashion, so that the formula is symmetrical with respect to them. On the other hand r_{xz} stands alone, being the *unique r*.

The formula $\dfrac{r_{23.1} - r_{24.1} r_{34.1}}{\sqrt{1 - r_{24.1}^2}\ \sqrt{1 - r_{34.1}^2}}$ relates to the four vari-

ables x_1, x_2, x_3, and x_4. Which of these variables are symmetrically treated in it? Which are unique? Without any idea of what these symbols represent we can study the pattern of this formula and venture a guess as to the answer for this question. Later we will attempt to verify the result of this guess. First we observe that the number 1 is treated in a way that is different from the treatment of other numbers, it always occurs after a period (whatever that may mean) and alone. Then we observe that $r_{24.1}$ and $r_{34.1}$ receive the same treatment, that the formula is symmetrical with respect to them, while $r_{23.1}$ stands alone, is unique. But in $r_{23.1}$ the numbers 2 and 3 seem to be symmetrical unless order is important (we set that down as a question which needs an answer) and in the symmetrical r's the variables 2 and 3 seem to receive the same treatment. It looks as though we might say that $r_{23.1}$ is unique, $r_{24.1}$ and $r_{34.1}$ symmetrical, that x_2 and x_3 are symmetrical, x_1 and x_4 unique.

To verify this we may interchange the variables, but first it will be necessary to know something about how these subscripts are used. We will now state, arbitrarily, with no attempt at explanation, that the subscripts in front of the period are called primary subscripts, and those following the period secondary subscripts, and that the order of the primary subscripts may be changed without affecting the value of the r, and that the order of the secondary subscripts may be changed without affecting the value of r. However if primary and secondary subscripts are exchanged, the value of r is affected. Thus $r_{12.345} = r_{21.435} = r_{21.534}$, etc. but $r_{12.345}$ is not equal to $r_{13.425}$, or $r_{52.134}$ or $r_{23.145}$, etc. This will have to be accepted without proof.

To verify our hypothesis that the formula is symmetrical with respect to x_2 and x_3, we will exchange 2 and 3 and examine the result. We have now $\dfrac{r_{32.1} - r_{34.1}r_{24.1}}{\sqrt{1 - r_{34.1}^2}\,\sqrt{1 - r_{24.1}^2}}$ which is the same as the original expression since $r_{23.1}$ is to be considered the same as $r_{32.1}$. If we interchange any other pair of variables, we produce an expression which is not equal to the first one. Hence x_2 and x_3 is the only pair of variables treated symmetrically here.

Homogeneity. It is to be understood that x^3, $2y^3$, x^2y, $7xy^2$, and $\frac{1}{2}xyz$ is each a term of the third degree; that x^4, $6x^3y$, $5x^2y^2$, $3xyz^2$, and $7xyzw$ is each a term of the fourth degree; that x^5, $\frac{1}{3}x^4y$, $8x^3y^2$, $\frac{2}{3}xy^2z^2$, $4x^3yz$, and $20\ xyzwv$ is each a term of the fifth degree. A term in which no variable occurs, as 3 or $3a$ (if a is a constant) is a term of zero degree, because we may think of 3 as meaning $3x^0$, or $3y^0$, or even $3x^0y^0z^0$. In general, the expression $kx^my^nz^rw^p$ is of degree $m+n+r+p$ if k is a constant and x, y, z, and w are variables. When all the terms in a polynomial are of the same degree, that expression is said to be *homogeneous.* Verify the fact that the following expressions are homogeneous:

$y^3 + 2xy^2 + yx^2$	(Each term is of third degree)
$\frac{1}{10}(x+y+z)$	(Each term is of first degree)
$4x^6 - x^2y^4 + xyz^2w^2$	(Each term is of sixth degree)
$3(x+y+z)^4$	(Each term in the expanded polynomial is of fourth degree)
$\left(\dfrac{x^2+y^2+z^2}{3}\right)^3$	(Each term in the expanded polynomial is of sixth degree)

Moments. In statistical work, much use is made of such expressions as $\frac{\Sigma x^2}{N}, \frac{\Sigma x^3}{N}, \frac{\Sigma x^4}{N}$, and the like. These expressions are called moments, and they are often designated by the small Greek letter μ (mu). Thus $\mu_2 = \frac{\Sigma x^2}{N}, \mu_3 = \frac{\Sigma x^3}{N}$, and in general $\mu_p = \frac{\Sigma x^p}{N}$. The subscript indicates the degree of the terms which are to be added. Then μ_3 represents the sum of terms of the third degree.

What does μ_3^2 represent? Study the following:

$$\mu_3 = \frac{\Sigma x^3}{N} = \frac{1}{N}(x_1^3 + x_2^3 + x_3^3 + \cdots + x_N^3)$$

$$\mu_3^2 = \frac{1}{N^2}(x_1^3 + x_2^3 + x_3^3 + \cdots + x_N^3)^2$$

$$\mu_3^2 = \frac{1}{N^2}(x_1^6 + x_2^6 + x_3^6 + \cdots + x_N^6 + 2x_1^3 x_2^3 + 2x_1^3 x_3^3 + \cdots + 2x_1^3 x_N^3 + \cdots + 2x_{N-1}^3 x_N^3)$$

Since $\frac{1}{N}$ and $\frac{1}{N^2}$ are constants, they have no effect upon the degree of any term. Consequently we see that μ_3^2 represents a polynomial all of whose terms are of the sixth degree. Also $\mu_6 = \frac{\Sigma x^6}{N}$ and represents a polynomial all of whose terms are of the sixth degree. Then $\mu_6 - \mu_3^2$ is a homogeneous expression.

Of what degree are the terms represented by $\mu_2 \mu_3$? Study the following:

$$\mu_2 = \frac{\Sigma x^2}{N} = \frac{1}{N}(x_1^2 + x_2^2 + \cdots + x_N^2)$$

$$\mu_3 = \frac{\Sigma x^3}{N} = \frac{1}{N}(x_1^3 + x_2^3 + \cdots + x_N^3)$$

$$\mu_2 \mu_3 = \frac{1}{N^2}(x_1^2 + x_2^2 + \cdots + x_N^2)(x_1^3 + x_2^3 + \cdots + x_N^3)$$

$$\mu_2 \mu_3 = \frac{1}{N^2}(x_1^5 + x_1^2 x_2^3 + \cdots + x_1^2 x_N^3 + x_1^3 x_2^2 + x_2^5 + \cdots + x_N^5)$$

Therefore $\mu_2\mu_3$ is seen to represent an expression in which every term is of fifth degree. Thus $\mu_5 - \mu_2\mu_3$ is a homogeneous expression. In general, then, we may say that

μ_p represents a sum of terms of degree p,

μ_p^2 represents a sum of terms of degree $2p$,

μ_p^q represents a sum of terms of degree qp,

$\mu_p\mu_q$ represents a sum of terms of degree $p+q$,

$\sqrt{\mu_p}$ represents a sum of terms of degree $\dfrac{p}{2}$

$\sqrt[q]{\mu_p}$ represents a sum of terms of degree $\dfrac{p}{q}$

$\dfrac{\mu_p}{\mu_q}$ represents a sum of terms of degree $p-q$

Exercise 40

Of what degree are the terms represented by each of the following expressions?

1. μ_7
2. $\mu_3\mu_5$
3. $(\mu_2)^3$
4. $\mu_4\mu_1$
5. μ_3^2
6. $\sqrt{\mu_4}$
7. $\sqrt{\mu_2}$
8. $\sqrt{\mu_6}$
9. $\dfrac{\mu_4}{\mu_2^2}$
10. $\mu_3\mu_4$
11. $\sqrt[3]{\mu_2}$
12. $(\mu_4)^3$
13. $\mu_a\mu_b$
14. $\mu_3 \div \mu_2$
15. $\mu_4 - \mu_2$
16. $\mu_3^2 \div \mu_2$

Pure Number. Such an expression as $\dfrac{\mu_4}{\mu_2^2}$ is of zero degree, and is consequently a pure number, uninfluenced by the units in which the variable may happen to be measured. Several such expressions are of great importance in statistical work. If we utilize this somewhat enlarged concept of the meaning of degree, we will accept the following conventions.

Mean $= \dfrac{\Sigma X}{N}$. This is a first degree expression (see Chapter XIII for definition of symbols).

$\sigma = \sqrt{\dfrac{\Sigma x^2}{N}} = \sqrt{\mu_2}$. This is a first degree expression.

Σxy is a second degree expression.

The concept of pure number, or of zero degree, gives meaning to many statistical formulas such as the following:

1. $r_{xy} = \dfrac{\Sigma xy}{N\sigma_x\sigma_y}$ has a second degree expression for its numerator and the product of two first degree expressions for its denominator. It is thus seen to be a pure number, the degree of its numerator and denominator being the same. This means that r_{xy} is the same, no matter what units are used for x and y.

2. $\dfrac{\sigma}{\text{Mean}}$ (which is sometimes called the "coefficient of variation") has a first degree term in both numerator and denominator, and is therefore a pure number.

3. $\dfrac{\sigma}{\sqrt{\text{Mean}}}$ is not a pure number, since the degree of its numerator is not the same as the degree of its denominator. This formula has been suggested as a substitute for $\dfrac{\sigma}{\text{Mean}}$ but commonly rejected because, not being a pure number, it is influenced by the unit in which the variable is measured.

4. $\dfrac{\mu_4 - \mu_2^2}{\mu_2^2}$ is a pure number. Its numerator is a homogeneous expression representing fourth degree terms, and its denominator also represents fourth degree terms. This number is useful in measuring the peakedness of frequency curves.

5. $\dfrac{\mu_3^2}{\mu_2^3}$ is an expression whose numerator and denominator each represent sixth degree terms, and it is consequently a pure number. This number is useful in measuring the skewness of frequency curves.

Order of a Correlation Coefficient. In statistical discussions of partial and multiple correlation, the concept of the *order* of a correlation coefficient is very useful. To clarify the statistical concept would require a rather long non-mathematical discussion which would be inappropriate to the plan of this book. However the general concept is so closely related to that of degree, of homogeneity and symmetry that it seems worth while to include it here, treating it in a fairly abstract manner, with no attempt to consider its practical significance.

r_{12} is a number which represents the correlation between x_1 and x_2 in general.

$r_{12.3}$ is a number which represents the net correlation between x_1 and x_2 when the influence of variation in x_3 has been eliminated.

$r_{12.34}$ is a number which represents the net correlation between x_1 and x_2 when the influence of variation in x_3 and x_4 has been eliminated.

$r_{12.3456 \ldots n}$ is a number which represents the net correlation between x_1 and x_2 when the influence of variation in x_3, x_4, x_5, x_6, $\cdots x_n$ has been eliminated.

σ_1 is a measure of the total variation in x_1.

$\sigma_{1.2}$ is a measure of the variation in x_1 which is not associated with variation in x_2.

$\sigma_{1.23}$ is a measure of the variation in x_1 which is not associated with variation in x_2 and x_3.

$\sigma_{1.234 \ldots n}$ is a measure of the variation in x_1 which is not associated with variation in x_2, x_3, x_4, $\cdots x_n$.

The number of secondary subscripts, i.e., subscripts following the period, gives the *order* of the correlation or the standard deviation. In a zero order correlation or standard deviation we have eliminated the influence of *no* other variables. For a *first order* correlation or standard deviation, we have eliminated the influence of *one* other variable. For a fifth order correlation or standard deviation, we have eliminated the influence of five other variables.

Rhythm and Pattern in Formulas. In the formulas for partial and multiple correlation and partial standard deviation there is a beautiful pattern and rhythm which can be appreciated and enjoyed by a person who is completely ignorant of their practical significance. The formula for a partial standard deviation of the fourth order is

$$\sigma_{1\cdot2345} = \sigma_1 \sqrt{1 - r_{12}^2} \sqrt{1 - r_{13\cdot2}^2} \sqrt{1 - r_{14\cdot23}^2} \sqrt{1 - r_{15\cdot234}^2}.$$

This can be extended to any number of variables. Note that the primary subscript in the left hand member, 1, occurs as a primary subscript in every term in the right hand member. There is one factor of the form $\sqrt{1-r^2}$ for each secondary subscript in the left hand member. In the first of these radicals we have a zero order r, in the second a first order r, and so on. Each secondary subscript of the left hand member serves in its turn as a primary subscript of an r, and after it has thus served it appears as a secondary subscript in every subsequent r in the formula.

Let us write the corresponding formula for $\sigma_{3\cdot21456}$, modeling it on the formula for $\sigma_{1\cdot2345}$. First we set down

$$\sigma_3 \sqrt{1-r_3^2} \sqrt{1-r_3^2} \sqrt{1-r_3^2} \sqrt{1-r_3^2} \sqrt{1-r_3^2}$$

as the general pattern. Then we insert the numbers 2, 1, 4, 5, and 6 successively as primary subscripts,

$$\sigma_3 \sqrt{1-r_{32}^2} \sqrt{1-r_{31}^2} \sqrt{1-r_{34}^2} \sqrt{1-r_{35}^2} \sqrt{1-r_{36}^2}.$$

Now to the r on the extreme right we annex 2, 1, 4, and 5 as secondary subscripts. To r_{35} we annex as secondary subscripts each primary subscript (except of course 3) occurring to its left, making it $r_{35\cdot214}$. Treating each r in this fashion gives us

$$\sigma_{3\cdot21456} =$$
$$\sigma_3 \sqrt{1-r_{32}^2} \sqrt{1-r_{31\cdot2}^2} \sqrt{1-r_{34\cdot21}^2} \sqrt{1-r_{35\cdot214}^2} \sqrt{1-r_{36\cdot2145}^2}.$$

EXERCISE 41

1. Of what order is each of the following:

(1) $r_{23.1}$ (6) $\sigma_{3.12456}$

(2) $\sigma_{4.56}$ (7) r_{13}

(3) σ_5 (8) $\sigma_{2.13}$

(4) r_{34} (9) σ_4

(5) $r_{34.5612}$ (10) $r_{56.1}$

2. Of what degree is each of the following:

(1) $x^3 y^2 z$ (5) $\dfrac{3xy^2}{z}$ (8) $\sqrt{xy}$ (11) $\dfrac{x^3}{\sqrt{y^6}}$

(2) $x^n y^m$ (6) $\dfrac{(x^3 y)^2}{z^4}$ (9) $(xy)^3$

(3) $\sqrt{y^3 z}$ (7) $\dfrac{x^4}{\sqrt{y^6}}$ (10) $\dfrac{x^n}{y^m}$ (12) $\dfrac{\sqrt{x^3 y}}{y^2}$

(4) $(x^2 y)^3$

3. Place a check in front of each of the following which is homogeneous:

—— (1) $x^2 + y^2 + z^2 + 2xy + 2xz + 2yz$

—— (2) $x^2 + y^2 + z^2 + 1$

—— (3) $x^2 - \dfrac{1}{x^2} + y^2 - \dfrac{1}{y^2}$

—— (4) $x^5 - 5x^3 y^2 + 5xy^4$

—— (5) $(x+y)^3$

—— (6) $(x+1)^3$

—— (7) $\Sigma x^2 - (\Sigma x)^2$

—— (8) $\Sigma x^4 - (\Sigma x^3)(\Sigma x)$

—— (9) $\mu_3 \mu_2 + \mu_6$

——(10) $\mu_2 + \sqrt{\mu_4}$

——(11) $(\mu_3)^2 + (\mu_2)^3 + \mu_2 \mu_3$

——(12) $\sqrt{\mu_6} + (\mu_6)^2$

——(13) $\dfrac{\mu_6}{\mu_2} - \dfrac{\mu_8}{\mu_4}$

——(14) $\dfrac{\mu_6}{\mu_2} - \mu_3$

——(15) $\sqrt{\mu_6} - 2\mu_3$

4. Using $\sigma_{1.2345} = \sigma_1 \sqrt{1 - r_{12}^2} \sqrt{1 - r_{13.2}^2} \sqrt{1 - r_{14.23}^2} \sqrt{1 - r_{15.234}^2}$ as a model, write the formula for

(1) $\sigma_{4.215}$ (2) $\sigma_{3.12}$ (3) $\sigma_{6.789}$

5. Using $R_{1(2345)} = \left\{ 1 - (1 - r_{12}^2)(1 - r_{13.2}^2)(1 - r_{14.23}^2)(1 - r_{15.234}^2) \right\}^{\frac{1}{2}}$ as a model, write the formula for

(1) $R_{2(34)}$ (2) $R_{5(4)}$ (3) $R_{3(256)}$

6. In each of the following there is a pair of symmetrical variables and one or more unique variables. Which variables are symmetrical and which unique? When numerical subscripts are used, it is to be understood that the variables are x_1, x_2, x_3, x_4, $\cdots x_n$.

(1) $x^2 y z^2 + x y^3 z$

(2) $(z + w + 2v)^2$

(3) $x^3 - y^3 + z + w$

(4) $x^v + x^w$

(5) $(\Sigma x)(\Sigma w) - (\Sigma x)(\Sigma y)(\Sigma w)$

(6) $r_{42.36} = \dfrac{r_{42.3} - r_{46.3} r_{26.3}}{\sqrt{1 - r_{46.3}^2} \sqrt{1 - r_{26.3}^2}}$

(7) $r_{23.45} \dfrac{\sigma_{2.45}}{\sigma_{3.45}}$

SECOND TEST

1. Place a check mark in front of each homogeneous expression:

—— (1) $x^2 + y^2 + z^2 + xyz$

—— (2) $x^2 + y^2 + z^2 + xy + xz + yz$

—— (3) $y^4 + y^3 x + x^2 y^2 + 10$

—— (4) $xy^4 + x^2 y^3 + y^5$

—— (5) $y^2 - 2y + 1$

—— (6) $\Sigma x^6 + (\Sigma x^3)^2$

—— (7) $\mu_3^2 - \mu_2^3$ where $\mu_3 = \dfrac{\Sigma x^3}{N}$ and $\mu_2 = \dfrac{\Sigma x^2}{N}$

—— (8) $\mu_5 - \mu_3^2$ where $\mu_5 = \dfrac{\Sigma x^5}{N}$ and $\mu_3 = \dfrac{\Sigma x^3}{N}$

—— (9) $\mu_{2n} - \mu_n^2$ where $\mu_{2n} = \dfrac{\Sigma x^{2n}}{N}$ and $\mu_n = \dfrac{\Sigma x^n}{N}$

——(10) $\mu_{n+2} - \mu_n^2$ where $\mu_{n+2} = \dfrac{\Sigma x^{n+2}}{N}$ and $\mu_n = \dfrac{\Sigma x^n}{N}$

2. Place a check mark in front of each expression symmetrical with respect to x and y.

——(1) $x^3 + 3x^2y + 3xy^2 + y^3$

——(2) $y - 2x$

——(3) $x^3 - y^3$

——(4) $x^3y + y^3x + 3$

——(5) $a^x + a^y$

——(6) $\dfrac{\Sigma xy}{N\sigma_x\sigma_y}$

——(7) $\dfrac{\Sigma xy}{N} - M_xM_y$

——(8) $(\Sigma x)^2 - \Sigma y^2$

——(9) $M_x - M_y + M_{x-y}$

3. A familiar statistical formula is

$$R_{1(234)} = \left\{ 1 - (1 - r_{12}^2)(1 - r_{13.2}^2)(1 - r_{14.23}^2) \right\}^{\frac{1}{2}}$$

Do not try to understand this formula, but using it as a model, write the formula for $R_{3(124)}$.

4. Consider that r_{12} and σ_1 are of zero order

$r_{12.3}$ and $\sigma_{1.2}$ are of first order

$r_{12.34}$ and $\sigma_{1.23}$ are of second order

$r_{12.345}$ and $\sigma_{1.234}$ are of third order, and so on.

Place a check mark in front of each expression in which all the r's and σ's are of the same order.

——(1) $\dfrac{r_{34.5} - r_{36.5}r_{46.5}}{\sqrt{1 - r_{36.5}^2}\sqrt{1 - r_{46.5}^2}}$

——(2) $(1 - r_{23}^2)(1 - r_{24.3}^2)(1 - r_{25.34}^2)$

——(3) $r_{12.34}\dfrac{\sigma_{1.34}}{\sigma_{2.34}}$

——(4) $r_{34.567}\dfrac{\sigma_{3.4567}}{\sigma_{4.3567}}$

5. There are three variables designated as x_1, x_2, and x_3. The formula $\dfrac{r_{13} - r_{12}r_{32}}{\sqrt{1 - r_{12}^2}\sqrt{1 - r_{32}^2}}$ is the formula for the correlation between two of them when the influence of the third is eliminated. Without trying to understand what the formula means, decide which of the variables is unique. Which of the r's is unique?

6. The formula $r_{34.56} = \dfrac{r_{34.5} - r_{36.5}r_{46.5}}{\sqrt{1 - r_{36.5}^2}\sqrt{1 - r_{46.5}^2}}$ relates to the variables x_3, x_4, x_5, and x_6. Which two are treated symmetrically?

XX

FITTING A STRAIGHT LINE TO A SWARM OF POINTS

Residual. Plot the following points:

x	-6	-5	-4	-3	-2	-1	0	1	2	3	4	5	6	7	8	9
y	-10	-8	-7	-5	-4	-2	0	1	3	4	7	9	11	11	14	15

While these do not lie exactly on a straight line, they cluster
closely around one. Hold a black thread tightly stretched,
and move it about among the points until you think you
have the position of the straight line which best represents
them. Draw this line and find its equation.

Let us suppose that in finding this equation one person
has secured the solution $y = \frac{3}{2}x$ and another $y = \frac{7}{4}x$. Which is
preferable? Evidently there is no single line which passes
through all the points, but there may be a line which fits
them better than any other does. Let us consider the pairs
of numbers given above to be values obtained by actual
observation on some physical phenomenon. Now for each
value of x given there we will estimate a theoretical value
of y from the equation $y = \frac{3}{2}x$. Clearly there will be discrepancies between these observed and estimated values. There
will, however, be discrepancies if y is estimated from the
equation $y = \frac{7}{4}x$, or from any other linear equation. The
difference between an observed value of y and a value estimated from an equation is known as a *residual*. We must
examine the sizes of the residuals for the two equations
$y = \frac{3}{2}x$ and $y = \frac{7}{4}x$.

Plot the pairs of numbers which represent observed values
and on the same axes draw the graph of $y = \frac{3}{2}x$. If a plotted

point does not lie on the graph, draw a vertical line parallel to OY from the point to the graph. Do this for all the points which are not exactly upon the line. You now have a graphic representation of the set of residuals, or discrepancies between observed values of y and values estimated from the equation $y = \frac{3}{2}x$. Table VII shows the arithmetic value of these

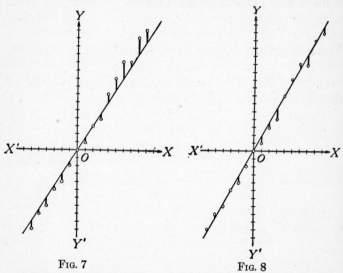

FIG. 7

Residuals from the line $y = \frac{3}{2}x$

FIG. 8

Residuals from the line $y = \frac{7}{4}x$

residuals and the squares of the residuals. The use of their squares will be explained later. Table VIII shows the residuals and their squares when y is estimated from the equation $y = \frac{7}{4}x$. Figures 7 and 8 show graphically the residuals from these two lines. A comparison of the two tables shows that in one case the sum of the residuals is 3.00 and in the other case -3.00, and we are not able to choose between the equations on this basis. The difficulty is that positive and negative residuals balance each other to such an extent

that their sum is not very enlightening. In order to judge
the real extent of the discrepancy between observed and
theoretical values we must get rid of the negative signs,
and we can do this by squaring the residuals. When that is
done we see readily that $y = \frac{1}{4}x$ is a better fit than $y = \frac{3}{2}x$,
because it gives a smaller sum for the squared residuals. Ex-
amination of Figures 7 and 8 also confirms this judgment, for we see there that the totality of the residuals
in Figure 7 is larger than the totality of the residuals in
Figure 8. We shall now investigate the possibility that
some other line may fit the set of points better than either
of these, at the same time developing a general method for
finding the straight *line of best fit*.

TABLE VII

RESIDUALS AND SQUARES OF RESIDUALS

$$y = \frac{3}{2}x$$

x	Observed Value of y	Estimated Value of y	Residual	Square of Residual
-6	-10	-9	$+1.00$	1.00
-5	-8	$-7\frac{1}{2}$	$+0.50$	0.25
-4	-7	-6	$+1.00$	1.00
-3	-5	$-4\frac{1}{2}$	$+0.50$	0.25
-2	-4	-3	$+1.00$	1.00
-1	-2	$-1\frac{1}{2}$	$+0.50$	0.25
0	0	0	0.00	0.00
1	1	$1\frac{1}{2}$	$+0.50$	0.25
2	3	3	0.00	0.00
3	4	$4\frac{1}{2}$	$+0.50$	0.25
4	7	6	-1.00	1.00
5	9	$7\frac{1}{2}$	-1.50	2.25
6	11	9	-2.00	4.00
7	11	$10\frac{1}{2}$	-0.50	0.25
8	14	12	-2.00	4.00
9	15	$13\frac{1}{2}$	-1.50	2.25
			-3.00	18.00

TABLE VIII

RESIDUALS AND SQUARES OF RESIDUALS

$$y = \tfrac{7}{4}x$$

x	Observed Value of y	Estimated Value of y	Residual	Square of Residual
−6	−10	−10½	−0.50	.2500
−5	− 8	− 8¾	−0.75	.5625
−4	− 7	− 7	0.00	.0000
−3	− 5	− 5¼	−0.25	.0625
−2	− 4	− 3½	+0.50	.2500
−1	− 2	− 1¾	+0.25	.0625
0	0	0	0.00	.0000
1	1	1¾	+0.75	.5625
2	3	3½	+0.50	.2500
3	4	5¼	+1.25	1.5625
4	7	7	0.00	.0000
5	9	8¾	−0.25	.0625
6	11	10½	−0.50	.2500
7	11	12¼	+1.25	1.5625
8	14	14	0.00	.0000
9	15	15¾	+0.75	.5625
			3.00	6.0000

Least Squares. A fundamental principle of wide applicability in fitting mathematical curves to observed data is the famous principle of least squares, which holds that the line of "best fit" is the one for which the sum of the squares of the residual errors is the least. We will now try to see if there is some other equation which may fit these values even better than the equation $y = \tfrac{7}{4}x$.

Let $y = mx + k$ be the general form of the equation we are seeking. We have sixteen pairs of values for x and y, but no values for m and k. If we substitute in $y = mx + k$ the values of x and y given by the first pair of coördinates (−6, −10), we have $-10 = -6m + k$. In the same way fifteen other equations can be found, such as

$-10 = -6m+k$
$-\ 8 = -5m+k$
$-\ 7 = -4m+k$
$-\ 5 = -3m+k$
and so on.

Obviously these equations are inconsistent. By the methods of the calculus it can be shown that the "best" values for m and k are given by the two equations:

$$\Sigma y = m\Sigma x + Nk$$
$$\Sigma yx = m\Sigma x^2 + k\Sigma x$$

Here $N = 16$, and Σy, Σx, Σx^2, and Σxy are numbers which can be found from the data, as in the computation below. Here we find

$$\Sigma x = 24 \qquad\qquad \Sigma xy = 635$$
$$\Sigma y = 39 \qquad\qquad \Sigma x^2 = 376$$

Since Σx and Σy are not zero, it is apparent that x and y cannot be representing the deviation of statistical variates from their means. If we wish to think of x and y as representing statistical variates, we could apply primes to the letters throughout, recognizing that deviations are taken from zero, which is an assumed mean. However, x and y are commonly used in algebra to represent deviations from zero, and we may omit the primes because we are using algebraic rather than statistical language.

We may now substitute the computed values of Σx, Σy, Σxy, and Σx^2 in the equations

x	y	xy	x^2
-6	-10	60	36
-5	$-\ 8$	40	25
-4	$-\ 7$	28	16
-3	$-\ 5$	15	9
-2	$-\ 4$	8	4
-1	$-\ 2$	2	1
0	0	0	0
1	1	1	1
2	3	6	4
3	4	12	9
4	7	28	16
5	9	45	25
6	11	66	36
7	11	77	49
8	14	112	64
9	15	135	81
24	39	635	376

$$\Sigma y = m\Sigma x + Nk$$

$\Sigma xy = m\Sigma x^2 + k\Sigma x$, and the latter become

$$39 = \ \ 24m + 16k$$
$$635 = 376m + 24k.$$

To solve these for m and k, we may multiply the first by 3 and the second by 2, obtaining two equations in which k

has the same coefficient, and then may subtract one equation from the other:

$$117 = 72m + 48k$$
$$1270 = 752m + 48k$$
$$\overline{1153 = 680m}$$
$$m = 1.696$$
$$k = -0.1065$$

Therefore our "best" equation is $y = 1.696x - 0.1065$.

With this equation compute values of y corresponding to the given values of x, find the residuals, or discrepancies between these computed values of y and the observed values. Find the sum of the squares of the residuals, and compare it with the sum in Table VII and in Table VIII.

More complicated equations can be fitted by processes similar to these, but they will not be treated here.

EXERCISE 42

Find the "best fitting" linear equation for each of the following sets of points, using the equations $\left\{ \begin{array}{l} \Sigma y = m\Sigma x + Nk \\ \Sigma xy = m\Sigma x^2 + k\Sigma x \end{array} \right\}$ to find m and k. Plot the points. Draw the graph of the equation through the points.

1.

x	-4	-3	-2	-1	0	1	2	3	4
y	10	9	8	6	2	0	-1	-5	-5

2.

x	$-7\frac{1}{2}$	-7	-6	-5	-5	-4	$-3\frac{1}{2}$	-3	-2	-2	-1	0	1	1	2	3
y	0	1	1	2	$1\frac{1}{2}$	2	$2\frac{1}{2}$	3	3	$3\frac{1}{2}$	4	5	$5\frac{1}{2}$	6	7	8

3.

x	-2	$-1\frac{1}{2}$	$-1\frac{1}{2}$	-1	-1	-1	$-\frac{1}{2}$	$-\frac{1}{2}$	0	0	0	$\frac{1}{2}$	$\frac{1}{2}$	1	$1\frac{1}{2}$	$1\frac{1}{2}$
y	6	5	4	$3\frac{1}{2}$	3	$2\frac{1}{2}$	2	$1\frac{1}{2}$	0	$-\frac{1}{2}$	-1	-2	-3	-4	-5

4.

x	-1	-1	$-\frac{1}{2}$	$-\frac{1}{2}$	0	0	0	$\frac{1}{2}$	1	1	$1\frac{1}{2}$	$1\frac{1}{2}$	2	2	2
y	-3	-2	-2	-1	-1	0	1	1	2	3	3	4	4	5	6

XXI

THE "NORMAL" CURVE

Importance. Many frequency distributions can be fitted approximately by a curve which is commonly, though somewhat ambiguously, known as the normal curve.[1] While it would be a serious mistake to think that this curve furnishes a universal pattern to which all frequency distributions must conform, still it has very wide statistical uses, particularly in connection with sampling problems, and even in the more elementary texts in statistical method it is much discussed.

The derivation of the equation of the normal curve requires a much more extensive knowledge of mathematics than is assumed in the present treatise. For such a derivation, students are referred to works on the mathematical theory of probability.[2] Here we will consider only those properties of the curve which demand no mathematics beyond algebra for their understanding.

Equation. The equation of the normal curve is

$$y = \frac{N}{\sigma \sqrt{2\pi}} e^{-\frac{x^2}{2\sigma^2}}.$$

[1] The curve has many other names, such as curve of error, probability curve, and curve of normal probability. It is also called the Gaussian curve because Gauss (1777–1855) studied it extensively, and sometimes called the Laplacean curve because Laplace (1749–1827) derived its equation even before Gauss did. De Moivre, however (1667–1754), gave the first proof of the equation of the curve in 1733.

[2] See Coolidge, J. L., *An Introduction to Mathematical Probability*, Oxford, 1925; Fisher, Arne, *The Mathematical Theory of Probability*, New York, 1915, 1922; Rietz, H. L., *Handbook of Mathematical Statistics*, Boston, 1924; Whittaker, E. T., and Robinson, G., *The Calculus of Observations*, London, 1924; and Yule, G. U., *Introduction to the Theory of Statistics*, London, many editions.

Here y is the ordinate of the curve and x the abscissa. The letter π represents a constant which is the ratio of the circumference of a circle to its diameter, approximately 3.1416. On page 129 it was stated that e is a constant whose value is approximately 2.718. N and σ are the two parameters of the curve, being constant for any particular set of data. N represents the number of cases in the frequency distribution and σ is its standard deviation. The variables in the equation are therefore x and y, and all the other letters represent constants. However π and e are genuine constants, while N and σ are constant for a given curve but change from one curve to the next, and therefore are the parameters of the curve.

It is ordinarily convenient to use σ as the scale unit for the horizontal axis, so that we express x not as so many inches, feet, dollars, or pounds, but as so many σ's. To say that $x=0.45\sigma$ is the same as to say $\frac{x}{\sigma}=0.45$, and we usually express the abscissa as $\frac{x}{\sigma}$ rather than x. It is convenient to use $\frac{N}{\sigma}$ as the scale unit for the vertical axis, since $\frac{N}{\sigma}$ is a number which can be factored out of the right hand member of the equation for the curve.

Unit Normal Curve. To use a number as the unit of measure is tantamount to setting it equal to unity, or 1, in the equation. Consequently we often write the equation as

$$z=\frac{1}{\sqrt{2\pi}}e^{-\frac{1}{2}x^2},$$

a form which is known as the *unit normal curve.* Here we have let $N=1$ and $\sigma=1$.

Finding Ordinates of the Curve. To find values of the ordinate corresponding to given values of $\frac{x}{\sigma}$ we will make use of logarithms. First we will find the value of z, the ordinate of a unit normal curve, and from this we can find y, the ordinate of any normal curve by the formula $y = \dfrac{N}{\sigma} z$.

The person who has not studied logarithms may skip this paragraph and plot the curve from the values given on page 202.

$$\log \pi \quad = 0.49715$$
$$\log \sqrt{2\pi} = \tfrac{1}{2}(\log 2 + \log \pi) = 0.39909$$
$$\log \frac{1}{\sqrt{2\pi}} = -0.39909 = \overline{1}.60091$$
$$\log e \quad = \log 2.7183 = 0.43429$$
$$\log e^{-\frac{x^2}{2\sigma^2}} = -\frac{x^2}{2\sigma^2} \log e = -\frac{x^2}{\sigma^2}\left(\frac{\log e}{2}\right) = -\frac{x^2}{\sigma^2}(0.21715)$$

Therefore $\log z = \overline{1}.60091 - \dfrac{x^2}{\sigma^2}(0.21715)$

By the application of this last formula, and the use of a table of logarithms, we may now find the values for z as in Table IX. Note that when $\dfrac{x}{\sigma} = .5$ we have $\dfrac{-x^2}{\sigma^2}(0.21715)$ equal to $-.25(0.21715) = -.0543$. But since we usually write a logarithm with a positive mantissa, we change this to its equivalent $-1 + .9457$ and write $\overline{1}.9457$.

TABLE IX

COMPUTATION OF ORDINATES

$\dfrac{x}{\sigma}$	$\log e^{-\frac{x^2}{2\sigma^2}}$ $= -\dfrac{x^2}{\sigma^2}(0.21715)$	$\log z$	z
0	0	$\overline{1}.6009$	.399
.5	$\overline{1}.9457$	$\overline{1}.5466$	.352
1.0	$\overline{1}.7828$	$\overline{1}.3837$	.242
1.5	$\overline{1}.5114$	$\overline{1}.1123$	.130
2.0	$\overline{1}.1314$	$\overline{2}.7323$	.054
2.5	$\overline{2}.6428$	$\overline{2}.2437$	.018

This illustrates the process of finding ordinates. It is obvious that these values are too far apart to give a clear picture of the curve, and that intermediate values must be found. The person who wants practice in working with logarithms will wish to check the values of z given in Table X. Others may accept these values without checking them.

TABLE X

ORDINATES OF THE NORMAL CURVE

$\frac{x}{\sigma}$	Ordinate	$\frac{x}{\sigma}$	Ordinate	$\frac{x}{\sigma}$	Ordinate	$\frac{x}{\sigma}$	Ordinate
0.0	.399	1.0	.242	2.0	.054	3.0	.0044
0.1	.397	1.1	.218	2.1	.044	3.1	.0033
0.2	.391	1.2	.194	2.2	.035	3.2	.0024
0.3	.381	1.3	.171	2.3	.028	3.3	.0017
0.4	.368	1.4	.150	2.4	.022	3.4	.0012
0.5	.352	1.5	.130	2.5	.018	3.5	.0009
0.6	.333	1.6	.111	2.6	.014	3.6	.0006
0.7	.312	1.7	.094	2.7	.010	3.7	.0004
0.8	.290	1.8	.079	2.8	.008	3.8	.0003
0.9	.266	1.9	.066	2.9	.006	3.9	.0002

Drawing the Curve. In Table X which gives ordinates of the normal curve, we have the values of z corresponding to values of $\frac{x}{\sigma}$ at intervals of 0.1. Lay off on graph paper a horizontal scale on which tenths of σ can be read, letting it extend at least 3σ each way from the origin. Draw a vertical axis at the origin and lay off on it a scale from which hundredths can be read. This scale need not extend beyond 0.40, since the ordinate at the origin, z_0, is only 0.399 which means $0.399\frac{N}{\sigma}$. Plot one point for each pair of values, $\frac{x}{\sigma}$ being measured on the horizontal scale and z on the vertical. Since $\frac{x}{\sigma}$ is squared in the formula, z will be the same whether

$\frac{x}{\sigma}$ is positive or negative, and the curve is symmetrical with respect to the vertical axis. Therefore for every z we must plot two points, one for which $\frac{x}{\sigma}$ is positive, and one for which it is negative. After these points are plotted, draw a smooth curve through them.

Properties of the Curve. A number of properties of the curve are easily apparent without the aid of higher mathematics.

1. *The curve is symmetrical* with respect to the vertical axis, for its two halves could be made to coincide by folding. Positive deviations and negative deviations from the origin are equally frequent.

2. *The maximum is at the origin.* The mean, median, and mode coincide. (The mode is the abscissa of the highest point on the curve. The median is the abscissa of the point beyond which exactly half of the frequency, or area, lies. The mean is the abscissa of the center of equilibrium of the area under the curve, if it were balanced on a knife edge.)

3. *The curve approaches nearer and nearer to the horizontal axis as $\frac{x}{\sigma}$ increases, and as $\frac{x}{\sigma}$ decreases, but theoretically it never reaches the axis.*

4. *There are points of inflection at $x = \pm \sigma$.* Near the origin the curve is concave to the horizontal axis. Out near $\pm 3\sigma$ it is convex to the horizontal axis. The point where the change in curvature occurs is called the point of inflection. To find it approximately, lay the edge of a ruler so that it is tangent to the curve at the origin, and lying outside of the curve. Slide the ruler slowly along the curve, keeping it in a tangent position. At first the curve is concave to the ruler, and is not cut by it. Then there comes a time when the ruler cuts across the curve at the point of tangency. Mark the point at which this happens, and repeat the experiment

on the other half of the curve. Verify the fact that the abscissas of these two points are given by the equations $\frac{x}{\sigma} = 1$ and $\frac{x}{\sigma} = -1$, which are obviously the same as $x = \sigma$ and $x = -\sigma$.

Area under the Curve. The area lying between the curve and the horizontal axis is said to be "under the curve." If you have plotted your curve so that σ is a units on the horizontal scale and $\frac{N}{\sigma}$ is b units on the vertical scale, then the total area under the curve should contain ab of the area units. Probably you have laid off 10 spaces for σ, and have let the ordinate at the mean be 40 spaces, on squared paper. This would mean that $.40\frac{N}{\sigma} = 40$, so that $\frac{N}{\sigma} = 100$ spaces. If $\frac{N}{\sigma} = 100$ and $\sigma = 10$, then $N = 100 \times 10 = 1000$, and accordingly there should be 1000 little area units under the entire curve. These area units are probably but not necessarily squares. Count the squares under the curve to see that there are approximately 1000 of them.

TABLE XI

PROPORTION OF AREA OF GIVEN SEGMENT
OF THE NORMAL CURVE

$\frac{x}{\sigma}$	Proportion of Area	
	Between 0 and $\frac{x}{\sigma}$	Between $\pm\frac{x}{\sigma}$
0.00	.0000	.0000
0.30	.1179	.2358
0.50	.1915	.3830
0.675	.2500	.5000
1.00	.3413	.6826
1.50	.4332	.8664
2.00	.4772	.9544
2.50	.4938	.9876
3.00	.4987	.9974
3.50	.4998	.9996

What proportion of the area lies between the mean and $+\sigma$? Between the mean and 2σ? Between σ and 2σ?

What proportion of the area lies between $-\sigma$ and $+\sigma$? Between -2σ and $+2\sigma$? Between -3σ and $+3\sigma$?

By counting squares, verify the facts stated in Table XI. Your per cents should check with these for about two places.

Tables of Areas of the Normal Curve. Many texts in statistical method furnish a table of areas and ordinates of the normal curve similar to the small table shown here but more extensive. There are also several books of tables for statistical computers, in which tables of the normal curve are included. Foremost among such is Pearson's *Tables for Statisticians and Biometricians*, indispensable to the professional statistician. The beginner will find Holzinger's *Statistical Tables for Students in Education and Psychology* well adapted to his needs.

Such tables are always made up for a unit-normal curve, in which N and σ are taken as unity. Consequently they are applicable to any normal distribution no matter what values N and σ may have. For the unit-normal distribution, the total area under the curve is 1, instead of N. The tables present three values:

(a) the abscissa, or $\frac{x}{\sigma}$,

(b) the ordinate, often called z,

(c) some area value.

Table XII is a small portion of such a table, extending from $x = 1.25\sigma$ to $x = 1.34\sigma$ by intervals of 0.01, where $\frac{x}{\sigma}$ is the argument. Table XIII is a small portion of a second table arranged with the area as argument, extending from an area of .245 to an area of .254, by intervals of 0.001. It will be seen that the first table is more convenient for solving some problems, the second more convenient for others.

TABLE XII

A Small Portion of a Table of Ordinates and Areas of the Normal Curve in Terms of Deviates from the Mean

$\dfrac{x}{\sigma}$	Area from 0 to $\dfrac{x}{\sigma}$	z	$\dfrac{x}{\sigma}$	Area from 0 to $\dfrac{x}{\sigma}$	z
1.25	.3944	.1826	1.30	.4032	.1714
1.26	.3962	.1804	1.31	.4049	.1691
1.27	.3980	.1781	1.32	.4066	.1669
1.28	.3997	.1758	1.33	.4082	.1647
1.29	.4015	.1736	1.34	.4099	.1626

TABLE XIII

A Small Portion of a Table of Deviates and Ordinates of the Normal Curve in Terms of Area from the Mean

Area from 0 to $\dfrac{x}{\sigma}$	$\dfrac{x}{\sigma}$	z	Area from 0 to $\dfrac{x}{\sigma}$	$\dfrac{x}{\sigma}$	z
.245	0.6588	.3211	.250	0.6745	.3178
.246	0.6620	.3204	.251	0.6776	.3171
.247	0.6651	.3198	.252	0.6808	.3164
.248	0.6682	.3191	.253	0.6840	.3157
.249	0.6713	.3184	.254	0.6871	.3151

Probable Error. In problems that relate to sampling, considerable interest attaches to the points which mark off the middle half of the area under the normal curve. Find the points which are 0.67σ on either side of the mean, draw ordinates at these points, and count the squares lying between these ordinates. The distance 0.6745σ is commonly called the *probable error*. The name *der wahrscheinliche Fehler* was used in 1815 in a German astronomical work to mean an error in the observation of the position of a heavenly body, the error to be of such a size that half of the errors made were likely to be larger than this and half smaller. The term "probable error" a translation of that phrase, has been in use well over a century. The probable error is sometimes used instead of the standard deviation as a scale unit for the horizontal axis.

Reading Tables of the Normal Curve. The following examples illustrate typical problems for which such tables are used. Each of these examples has a host of practical applications, which are not developed here because this book does not deal with the content of statistical method. It must be understood that the examples shown here are set down solely for practice in the reading of tables, and not as models to be followed in an applied problem. Many real problems do not warrant so great an appearance of precision as is implied here. The narrow limits of the small sections of the tables from which we are working impose these conditions.

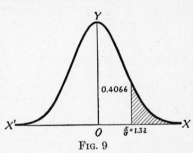

FIG. 9

1. In a normal distribution, what proportion of the measures exceed the mean by 1.32σ or more?

From Table XII we learn that 0.4066 of the total area lies between the mean and $x = 1.32\sigma$. Now since 0.5 of the area lies above the mean, or 0.5 of the measures exceed the mean, the proportion exceeding the mean by 1.32σ or more should be $0.5000 - 0.4066 = 0.0934$, or approximately 9%. It must be noted that we have treated 1.32σ as an ideal mathematical point having no width, a point which merely divides the horizontal axis into two portions as its ordinate divides the area into two portions. See Figure 9.

2. In a normal distribution with mean $= 52.32$ and $\sigma = 4.50$,

what proportion of the individuals would have scores between 46.30 and 58.00?

The question must be broken up into two questions.

(1) What proportion would have scores between 46.30 and the mean?

$$\frac{x_1}{\sigma} = \frac{46.30 - 52.32}{4.5} = \frac{-6.02}{4.5} = -1.34$$

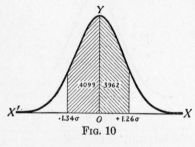
Fig. 10

In Table XII we read that 0.4099 is the proportion of area between 0 and $x = 1.34\sigma$. Since the curve is symmetrical, the area between 0 and $x = -1.34\sigma$ is obviously also 0.4099. See Figure 10.

(2) What proportion would have scores between the mean and 58.00?

$$\frac{x_2}{\sigma} = \frac{58.00 - 52.32}{4.5} = \frac{5.68}{4.5} = 1.26$$

Table XII tells us that 0.3962 is the proportion of area between 0 and $x = 1.26\sigma$.

Therefore between -1.34σ and $+1.26\sigma$ the proportion of area is $0.4099 + 0.3962 = 0.8061$ or about 81%.

3. In a normal distribution with mean $= 69.3$ and $\sigma = 2.4$, what proportion of the individuals would have scores between 72.3 and 72.5? (The limitations of our table, which covers only a very narrow range, makes it necessary to use as illustration such special values as these. In practice such a question would be warranted only with a very large sample in which the distribution was exactly normal, a condition not often realized.)

(1) What proportion of the area is between the mean and 72.5?

$$\frac{x_2}{\sigma} = \frac{72.5 - 69.3}{2.4} = 1.33$$

The area between 0 and x_2 is therefore 0.4082.

(2) What proportion of area is between the mean and 72.3?

$$\frac{x_1}{\sigma} = \frac{72.3 - 69.3}{2.4} = 1.25$$

The area between 0 and x_1 is therefore 0.3944.

The area between x_1 and x_2 is $0.4082 - 0.3944 = 0.0138$ or approximately 1%.

4. Interpolate to find an approximate value of the ordinate at $x = 1.326\sigma$.

Ordinate at $1.32\sigma = 0.1669$
"   " $1.33\sigma = 0.1647$

Now 1.326 is 0.6 of the way from 1.32 to 1.33. Consequently the ordinate at 1.326σ should be approximately 0.6 of the way from 0.1669 to 0.1647. The difference is 0.0022, and $(0.6)(.0022) = 0.00132$. The ordinate is therefore approximately $0.1669 - 0.00132$ or 0.1656. Note that we subtract the correction because the ordinates are decreasing as the values of $\frac{x}{\sigma}$ increase. Note also that we do not attempt to get an interpolated value of more than four places.

5. If the mean of a normal distribution is 69.3 and σ is 2.4, between what values, symmetrically placed on either side of the mean, does one-half of the area lie? Here the problem is reversed, and Table XIII will be more helpful. We are to center our attention upon a symmetrical strip of area which is to contain 0.50 of the total area. Sketch a normal curve and draw an ordinate at the mean. Then

mark on the base line a point x_1 such that an ordinate at that point divides the area below the mean into two equal parts. Mark on the base line a second point x_2 such that an ordinate at x_2 divides the area above the mean into two equal parts. The area from the mean to x_2 should therefore be equal to the area from x_1 to the mean, and each should equal 0.25 of the total area. In Table XIII we read that the abscissas of the points we seek are $\pm 0.6745\sigma$. The sign $\pm$ is read "plus or minus" and is used to indicate simultaneously the positive and negative values of the same number. Here it means that one required value is $+0.6745\sigma$ and the other is -0.6745σ. Now

$$0.6745\sigma = 0.6745(2.4) = 1.6188,$$

or better, 1.62. $x_1 = 69.3 - 1.62$ or 67.7, and

$$x_2 = 69.3 + 1.62 \text{ or } 70.9,$$

which are the values sought.

In studies of sampling, the deviation from the mean between whose positive and negative values one-half the area of a normal curve lies, is called the *probable error*, usually designated as *p.e.*

$$p.e. = 0.6745\sigma.$$

6. Interpolate to find an approximate value of $\dfrac{x}{\sigma}$ when the area between the mean and $\dfrac{x}{\sigma}$ is 0.2462.

When area $= 0.246$ $\dfrac{x}{\sigma} = 0.6620$

When area $= 0.247$ $\dfrac{x}{\sigma} = 0.6651$

Now 0.2462 is 0.2 of the way from 0.246 to 0.247. Consequently the value of $\dfrac{x}{\sigma}$ which we require should be approximately 0.2 of the way from 0.6620 to 0.6651. The difference is 0.0031 and $(0.2)(0.0031) = 0.00062$. The value sought is therefore approximately $0.6620+0.00062$ $=0.6626$. Note that we add the correction because $\frac{x}{\sigma}$ is increasing as the area increases.

7. If the mean of a normal distribution is 106.2 and σ is 12.3, what score would be exceeded by 74.8% of the members of the group? The mean is exceeded by 50% of such a group. There-

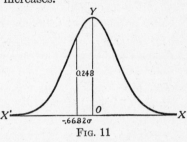

Fig. 11

fore the proportion scoring between the mean and the unknown score should be 24.8% or 0.248, as in Figure 11. In Table XIII we see that if the area between 0 and $\frac{x}{\sigma}$ is 0.248, $\frac{x}{\sigma}=0.6682$. Then $x=0.6682(12.3)=8.21886$, or better 8.22. The score in question is therefore $106.2-8.22$ $=98.0$.

Exercise 43

1. What proportion of the area under a normal curve

    (1) Lies between 1.27σ and 1.33σ?

    (2) Lies between -1.31σ and -1.25σ?

    (3) Lies between -1.29σ and $+1.29\sigma$?

    (4) Lies between -1.28σ and $+1.26\sigma$?

    (5) Lies above 1.30σ?

    (6) Lies below 1.28σ?

    (7) Lies above -1.26σ?

    (8) Lies below -1.33σ?

2. Between what limits does the middle 49% of the area of a normal curve lie?

3. Below what abscissa point does 75.3% of the area of a normal curve lie?

4. Above what abscissa point does 75.1% of the area of a normal curve lie?

5. Above what abscissa point does 25.4% of the area of a normal curve lie?

6. Below what abscissa point does 24.6% of the area of a normal curve lie?

7. The mean of a normal distribution is 113.30 and σ is 5.6.

    (1) Between what limits does the middle 50.8% of the area lie?
    (2) Between what limits does the middle 49.2% of the area lie?
    (3) What proportion of the scores are less than 120.30?
    (4) What score is exceeded by 24.7% of the cases?
    (5) What score is exceeded by 74.7% of the cases?
    (6) What score is exceeded by 75.3% of the cases?
    (7) What score is exceeded by 24.9% of the cases?
    (8) What limits include the middle half of the cases?

8. By interpolation find the values to fill the blank spaces in the following table:

$\dfrac{x}{\sigma}$	Area between 0 and $\dfrac{x}{\sigma}$
1.332	
0.660	
1.257	
0.670	
	.4000
	.2493
	.4070
	.2536

ANSWERS

Chapter I

First Test, page 3

1. $+$	7. $+$	13. 0	19. $+$
2. 0	8. 0	14. $+$	20. 0
3. $+$	9. $+$	15. 0	21. 0
4. 0	10. $+$	16. 0	22. $+$
5. 0	11. 0	17. $+$	23. $+$
6. $+$	12. $+$	18. $+$	24. 0

Exercise 1, page 6

1. $\frac{5}{3}$ or $1\frac{2}{3}$

2. $\frac{21}{16}$ or $1\frac{5}{16}$

3. $\frac{77}{30}$ or $2\frac{17}{30}$

4. $\frac{7}{20}$

5. 51

6. $15\frac{2}{5}$

7. $10\frac{1}{3}$

8. 12

9. 14

10. $\frac{18}{5} + \frac{12}{7}$ or $5\frac{11}{35}$

11. $\frac{4}{25}$

12. 6

13. $\frac{1}{4}$

14. 5

15. $\frac{8}{14}$ or $\frac{4}{7}$

16. $\sqrt{0.96}$

17. $\sqrt{0.91}$

18. $\sqrt{0.19}$

Second Test, page 6

1. $+$	7. $+$	13. 0	19. $+$
2. 0	8. $+$	14. $+$	20. 0
3. $+$	9. 0	15. 0	21. 0
4. 0	10. 0	16. 0	22. $+$
5. 0	11. 0	17. $+$	23. $+$
6. $+$	12. $+$	18. 0	24. 0

Chapter II

First Test, page 7

1. (1) 6

(2) 3

(3) 3

(4) 1

(5) 4

(6) 4

(7) 4

(8) ?

(9) 2

First Test, page 7, *continued*

2. (1) 593000
 (2) 43.5
 (3) 4.73
 (4) 5.70
 (5) 43400

 (6) 53400
 (7) 130.
 (8) 4.00
 (9) 0.00462

3. (1) 5.359
 (2) 29.9
 (3) 15.42
 (4) 310 or 315

 (5) 3500 or 3510
 (6) 2425.6

Exercise 2, page 14

1. (1) ✕
 (2) 0
 (3) 0
 (4) 0

 (5) 0
 (6) ✕
 (7) ✕
 (8) 0

2. (1) 2
 (2) 5
 (3) 5
 (4) 5

 (5) 2
 (6) 3
 (7) 5
 (8) 2

 (9) ?
 (10) ?
 (11) 3
 (12) 3

3. (1) 5689000
 (2) 437600
 (3) 0.01234
 (4) 29.00

 (5) 99.00
 (6) 2.568
 (7) 5.344
 (8) 5.346

 (9) 5.347
 (10) 3.000
 (11) 489000
 (12) 32100

4. (1) 1710
 (2) 17.1
 (3) 2.03
 (4) 7.924

 (5) 4.9
 (6) 0.7
 (7) 0.038
 (8) 0.0018

 (9) 75
 (10) 84
 (11) 3424.5
 (12) 22.2

5. (1) As many as you please
 (2) 4
 (3) 3
 (4) 2
 (5) 4 (which completes the square)
 (6) 6 (which completes the cube)

 (7) 2
 (8) 4
 (9) 3
 (10) 2

CHAPTER II, *continued*

Second Test, page 16

1. (1) 5
   (2) 4
   (3) 2
   (4) 1
   (5) 3
   (6) 4
   (7) 5
   (8) ?
   (9) 2

2. (1) 23.8
   (2) 1.36
   (3) 28000
   (4) 36.3
   (5) 78.2
   (6) 21000
   (7) 0.000423
   (8) 90000 or $90\overline{0}00$
   (9) 1.39

3. (1) 52.7
   (2) 75.17
   (3) 20.40
   (4) 8.8
   (5) 0.37
   (6) 4580.9

CHAPTER III

First Test, page 17

1. 70.51
2. 20.63
3. 0.04493
4. 0.2938
5. 7.491
6. 63.25
7. 0.9487
8. 2.530
9. 18.97
10. 0.3162

Exercise 3, page 19

1. (1) $\overline{4}\,\overline{37}$
   (2) $\overline{43}\,\overline{70}$
   (3) $\overline{4.}\,\overline{37}$
   (4) $\overline{0.43}\,\overline{70}$
   (5) $\overline{0.}\,\overline{00}\,\overline{04}\,\overline{37}$
   (6) $\overline{12.53}\,\overline{75}\,\overline{10}$
   (7) $\overline{1}\,\overline{36.}\,\overline{40}$
   (8) $\overline{0.00}\,\overline{00}\,\overline{90}$
   (9) $\overline{90.}\,\overline{12}\,\overline{30}$
   (10) $\overline{5}\,\overline{67.}\,\overline{20}$
   (11) $\overline{0.35}$
   (12) $\overline{0.40}$
   (13) $\overline{3.21}\,\overline{40}$
   (14) $\overline{0.00}\,\overline{20}$
   (15) $\overline{0.10}$

2. 2, 6, 2, 6, 2, 3, 1, 9, 9, 2, 5, 6, 1, 4, 3

3. 2, 1, 3, 2, 3, 9, 2, 6, 7, 2, 1, 2, 9, 4, 1, 7

4. (1) 69.48
   (2) 37.40
   (3) 51.46
   (4) 31.14
   (5) 41.33
   (6) 4.428
   (7) 0.5522
   (8) 28.7
   (9) 236

Exercise 3, page 20, *continued*

5. (1) 305.10
   (2) 50.16
   (3) 6.050
   (4) 70.630

   (5) 9.051
   (6) 15.050
   (7) 2.070
   (8) 80.6100

6. (1) 279.20
   (2) 7.691
   (3) 1.594
   (4) 13.96
   (5) 219.60

   (6) 3.19800
   (7) 30.510
   (8) 270.3004
   (9) 3.80899

Second Test, page 22

1. 61.98
2. 30.45
3. 0.04589
4. 0.2686
5. 5.977

6. 94.87
7. 0.3162
8. 1.897
9. 26.65
10. 0.6325

CHAPTER IV

First Test, page 23

1. (1) 256.515
   (2) 8.1
   (3) ✕

   (4) 65.2
   (5) ✕
   (6) 0.0659

2. (1) 658

   (2) 0.0087

3. (1) 256.22

   (2) 8.113

4. (1) 43335900

   (2) 71.24

Exercise 4, page 28

1. 700	7. 60	13. 10	19. 0.09
2. 80	8. 0.2	14. 3	20. 20
3. 100	9. 0.6	15. 0.3	21. 90
4. 1000	10. 0.03	16. 1	22. 0.1
5. 30	11. 10	17. 0.06	23. 2
6. 4	12. 60	18. 0.3	24. 200

CHAPTER IV, *continued*

Exercise 5, page 30

4. (1) 8.83   (4) 2.55421   (7) 92.574
    (2) 8.06   (5) 65.57   (8) 2.56164
    (3) 0.8112   (6) 86.6   (9) 0.254951

5. (1) 43230600   (2) 85.3   (3) 0.00433491

Second Test, page 31

1. (1) 0.256320   (4) 0.084
    (2) ×   (5) 0.255930
    (3) 8.1   (6) ×

2. (1) 0.79   (2) 6.51

3. (1) 91.488   (2) 6.519

4. (1) 42.8109   (2) 0.872

CHAPTER V

First Test, page 32

1. 3	**5.** 1	**9.** 2	**12.** 1	**15.** 3
2. 2	**6.** 4	**10.** 1	**13.** 2	**16.** 2
3. 2	**7.** 3	**11.** 4	**14.** 4	**17.** 4
4. 1	**8.** 3			

Exercise 6, page 36

1. (1) 5.2   (6) 1.3   (11) 0.06   (16) 216.2
    (2) 17.5   (7) 50.7   (12) 20.14   (17) 0.5
    (3) 24   (8) 142.3   (13) 32   (18) 301.3
    (4) 102   (9) 9.1   (14) 0.51   (19) 94.2
    (5) 50.3   (10) 0.3   (15) 6.03   (20) 86.3

2. (1) 80%   (5) 250%   (9) 7.15%   (13) 5%
    (2) 75%   (6) 1.2%   (10) 65%   (14) 2%
    (3) 0.8%   (7) 17%   (11) 11.2%   (15) 7.5%
    (4) $3\frac{1}{3}$%   (8) 4.65%   (12) 90%

Chapter V, *continued*

Exercise 6, page 36, *continued*

3. (1) 240000 (6) 0.6 (11) 0.05 (16) 0.4
  (2) 50 (7) 0.0009 (12) 0.02 (17) 6
  (3) 0.0017 (8) 1600 (13) 20 (18) 50
  (4) 80 (9) 600 (14) 0.2 (19) 200
  (5) 600 (10) 200 (15) 3 (20) 0.01

4. (1) 2 (6) 2 (11) 4 (16) 3
  (2) 3 (7) 3 (12) 4 (17) 3
  (3) 1 (8) 1 (13) 4 (18) 4
  (4) 1 (9) 3 (14) 1 (19) 3
  (5) 2 (10) 1 (15) 4 (20) 2

Second Test, page 38

1. 3   **5.** 4   **9.** 2   **12.** 3   **15.** 4
2. 3   **6.** 3   **10.** 1   **13.** 2   **16.** 1
3. 2   **7.** 3   **11.** 1   **14.** 4   **17.** 1
4. 2   **8.** 3

Chapter VI

All answers should be verified by checking.

Chapter VII

First Test, page 52

1. (1) $\dfrac{x_1 x_3}{x_2 + x_4}$ (2) $x_1(x_2 + x_3 + x_4)$ (3) $(x_3 + x_4) - (x_1 + x_2)$

2. (1) $P = \dfrac{S}{1 + rt}$ (4) $V = \frac{1}{6}\pi d^3$ or $V = \dfrac{\pi d^3}{6}$
  (2) $d = 16t^2$ (5) $(n + n') - (n - n') = 2n'$
  (3) $F = 25 + 15(m - 1) + \frac{5}{3}w$
   or $F = 15m + \frac{5}{3}w + 10$

3. $S = 2P' + 3P'' + P'''$

4. $G_1 = F'_1 - F_1$

5. (1) $R = N - W$ (3) $R = N - W - Q$
  (2) $S = N - 2W$ (4) $S = N - 2W - Q$

CHAPTER VII, *continued*

Exercise 13, page 56

1. (1) $2n$

(2) $3+n$ or $n+3$

(3) $5n-7$

(4) n^2

(5) $\dfrac{6}{n}$ or $6/n$

(6) $\dfrac{20}{n+2}$

(7) $(n+5)(n-2)$

(8) $(2n)^2$ or $4n^2$

(9) $2n^2$

2. (1) $n_1+n_2+n_3+n_4$

(2) $n_1 n_2 n_3 n_4$

(3) $(n_1+n_2)(n_3+n_4)$

(4) $n_1 n_2 n_3 n_4-(n_1+n_2+n_3+n_4)$ or $n_1 n_2 n_3 n_4-n_1-n_2-n_3-n_4$

(5) $\dfrac{n_1+n_2}{n_3+n_4}$

(6) $n_1(n_2+n_3+n_4)$

(7) $\dfrac{n_3}{n_1+n_2+n_4}$

(8) $\dfrac{(10n_1)(4n_2)}{6n_3}$ or $\dfrac{40n_1 n_2}{6n_3}$ or $\dfrac{20n_1 n_2}{3n_3}$

4. x

$2x$

$2x+40$

$3(2x+40)=6x+120$

$6x+20$

$4x+20$

$\dfrac{4x+20}{4}=x+5$

5. x

$x+25$

$4(x+25)=4x+100$

$5x+100$

$x+20$

$2x+40$

$2x$

6. (1) $n_1+n_2=45$

(2) $x_1-x_2=6$

(3) $\dfrac{1}{2}x+\dfrac{1}{3}y=20$ or $\dfrac{x}{2}+\dfrac{y}{3}=20$

(4) $3n+7n=10n$

(5) $n_1+n_2+n_3=90$

(6) $N_G=N_B+5$ or $N_G-N_B=5$ or $N_G-5=N_B$

(7) $N_C=N_H+N_G+N_K$

(8) $8x-7x=x$

7. (1) $S=2lw+2lh+2wh$ or $S=2(lw+lh+wh)$

(2) $V=lwh$

(3) $i=Prt$

Exercise 13, page 58, *continued*

(4) $V_C = 25q + 10d + 5n + p$ (6) $C = \frac{5}{9}(F - 32)$

(5) $F = 15 + 10(q-1) + \dfrac{5w}{3}$ (7) $F = \frac{9}{5}C + 32$

     or $F = 10q + \dfrac{5w}{3} + 5$

Second Test, page 59

1. (1) $\dfrac{n_1 + n_2}{n_3}$ (2) $n_2(n_1 + n_3)$ (3) $n_1 n_2 n_3$

2. (1) $A = \dfrac{h}{2}(b_1 + b_2)$ (4) $C = 8 + 6(w-1)$ or $C = 6w + 2$

    (2) $A = P(1 + rt)$ (5) $3(n+n') + 5(n+n') = 8(n+n')$

    (3) $A = 4\pi r^2$

3. $S_T = s_1 + 3s_2 + 4s_3$

4. $G_5 = T_5' - T_5$

5. (1) $w = t - r$

    (2) $S = 2r - t$

    (3) $w = t - n - r$

    (4) $S = r - (t - n - r)$ or $S = 2r - t + n$

CHAPTER VIII

First Test, page 61

1. (1) $4a - b - 7c - 2x + 4$ (3) $-4a + 8n - 16$

    (2) $-4x - 10$ (4) $-2p + 4q - 6r + 2$

2. Check (3), (6), (7), (8), (9), (11), (15), (16), (18)

3. Check (1), (3), (6)

Exercise 14, page 63

1. $-5, -3.6, -0.7, -0.1, 0, 0.5, 2, 4.3$

2. $0, -0.1, 0.5, -0.7, 2, -3.6, 4.3, -5$

3. (1) -50 (3) $+7$ (5) $+12$

    (2) -14 (4) $+16$ (6) -5

4. (1) -36 (3) $+17$ (5) $+14$

    (2) -26 (4) -16 (6) -5

CHAPTER VIII, *continued*

Exercise 14, page 63, *continued*

  5. (1) $-x+6$

     (2) $p-3q-2r+s$

     (3) $3n-5r-2s$

  6. (1) $d+4f$

     (2) $6x-2y$

     (3) $2k-4t+7m+4-n$

Exercise 15, page 70

1.

(1) 15	(21) 4	(41) $-3a+6b$
(2) -42	(22) -4	(42) $6a^2b^2$
(3) -12	(23) $-\frac{1}{8}$	(43) $6x^2y-8xy^2$
(4) 9	(24) ±5	(44) $2a-2b-c$
(5) 0	(25) -9	(45) $x+8y-4$
(6) -14.4	(26) ±6	(46) $4n+9r+8$
(7) $3a^2$	(27) a	(47) $rn-5r-3n$
(8) 2	(28) a^3	(48) $-2ay+3ax-xy$
(9) -2	(29) $-a$	(49) $-a^2+ab-5ac$
(10) 9	(30) 6	(50) $-13+2x-4y$
(11) -4	(31) $30a^3$	(51) $ab+2bc$
(12) -1	(32) $16a^2$	(52) $-5p-6q+4$
(13) 16	(33) $-27x^3$	(53) $\frac{1}{2}-7\frac{1}{2}y+9\frac{z}{x}$
(14) 8	(34) $-72a^3-10a^2$	(54) $\frac{1}{2}-b+c$
(15) -8	(35) $-6x^3y^2$	(55) $-2x-1+3y$
(16) a^2	(36) $-12n^3$	(56) $-\frac{4}{3}x^2+a-\frac{2}{3}x$
(17) a^2	(37) $a+b$	(57) $-1+3x-4y$
(18) $-a^3$	(38) -3	(58) $-r+2s$
(19) 4	(39) $-3n$	(59) $19c-10a+3$
(20) 8	(40) pq	(60) $-8a+12b-6c$

2.

(1) 14	(4) -2	(7) -5.5	(10) 1.057
(2) 0	(5) 6	(8) $-\frac{4}{3}$	(11) 9.27
(3) 11	(6) -9	(9) -3	(12) $-.27$

Second Test, page 71

1. (1) $16n-10r+3p-12$

    (2) $-c+7d+2a$

    (3) $-12M_1-4M_2+2M_3$

    (4) $-\frac{3}{2}c+2d+\frac{9}{5}cd$

2. 2, 4, 5, 7, 10, 13, 15, 17

3. 1, 3, 6

CHAPTER IX

First Test, page 73

1. $\dfrac{\Sigma x'}{N}$

2. $Nr_{12}\sigma_1\sigma_2$

3. $n\sigma_p^2$

4. $\dfrac{\sigma_x^2+\sigma_y^2-\sigma_{x-y}^2}{2\sigma_x\sigma_y}$

5. $\sqrt{1-\dfrac{\sigma_{1\cdot2}^2}{\sigma_1^2}}$

6. $\pm\sqrt{1-(1-r_{12}^2)(1-r_{13\cdot2}^2)}$

7. $1-E_{xy}^2$

8. $\dfrac{r_1}{a-r_1(a-1)}$

9. $\dfrac{\Sigma x'y'}{N}-c_xc_y$

10. $\dfrac{\sigma_1^2}{\sigma_2^2}(r-1)+1$

Exercise 16, page 76

1. $\dfrac{b}{a}$

2. 14

3. 1.6

4. $\pm\dfrac{1}{b}\sqrt{cb^2-a^2}$

   or $\pm\sqrt{c-\dfrac{a^2}{b^2}}$

5. $\dfrac{a}{c^2}$

6. $\frac{2}{3}$

7. $\dfrac{ab-a_1(b_1^2+c_1^2)}{b_2^2+c_2^2}$

   or $\pm\sqrt{\dfrac{ab-a_1(b_1^2+c_1^2)-a_2b_2^2}{a_2}}$

8. $\dfrac{cx-dx}{bx-a}$ or $\dfrac{x(c-d)}{bx-a}$

9. 0.24

10. $\dfrac{2A}{b}$

11. -2

12. -3.944

13. 31.235

14. $-0.43a+\frac{14}{3}$

15. $6\frac{3}{8}$

16. -0.10385

Second Test, page 77

1. $1.4826p$

2. $r_{12}\dfrac{x_2}{\sigma_2}$

3. $N\sigma^2$

4. $\dfrac{\sigma_{a+b}^2-\sigma_a^2-\sigma_b^2}{2\sigma_a\sigma_b}$

5. $\sigma_1\sqrt{1-R_{1\cdot23}^2}$

6. r_{xy}^2

7. $\pm\sqrt{\dfrac{N_T\sigma_T^2-N_2(\sigma_2^2+d_2^2)-N_1d_1^2}{N_1}}$

8. $\dfrac{ar_1}{1+(a-1)r_1}$

9. $\dfrac{\Sigma(x')^2}{N}-c^2$

10. $\dfrac{S_1^2}{S_2^2}(r_1-1)+1$

CHAPTER X

First Test, page 79

1. (1) 0   (7) +   (13) +   (19) 0

(2) +   (8) +   (14) 0   (20) +

(3) 0   (9) 0   (15) 0   (21) 0

(4) +   (10) 0   (16) +   (22) +

(5) +   (11) 0   (17) +   (23) 0

(6) 0   (12) +   (18) +   (24) 0

2. $x = \dfrac{ac}{b}$

3. $r_1 = \dfrac{r_x}{n + r_x - nr_x}$

4. $n = 8\frac{2}{3}$

5. (1) S decreases

(2) S decreases

(3) A fraction smaller than 1, a positive number

(4) 0

(5) A fraction smaller than 1, a positive number

(6) A negative number

Exercise 17, page 85

1. $\frac{22}{15}$, $\frac{17}{24}$, $\frac{26}{21}$, $\frac{11}{4}$, $\frac{41}{63}$, $\frac{3}{2}$

2. $\dfrac{a}{b} + \dfrac{c}{d} = \dfrac{ad + bc}{bd}$

3. $\frac{8}{15}$, $\frac{1}{8}$, $\frac{8}{21}$, $\frac{15}{8}$, $\frac{2}{21}$, $\frac{5}{9}$

4. $\dfrac{a}{b} \cdot \dfrac{c}{d} = \dfrac{ac}{bd}$

5. $\frac{5}{6}$, $\frac{9}{8}$, $\frac{6}{7}$, $\frac{6}{5}$, $\frac{14}{9}$, $\frac{4}{5}$

6. $\dfrac{a}{b} \div \dfrac{c}{d} = \dfrac{ad}{bc}$

7. (1) $\frac{15}{20}$, just as large

(2) $\frac{10}{3}$, 5 times as large

(3) $\frac{2}{15}$, $\frac{1}{5}$ as large

(4) $\frac{10}{3}$, 5 times as large

Exercise 17, page 86, *continued*

(5) $\dfrac{ac}{bc}$, just as large

(6) $\dfrac{ac}{b}$, c times as large

(7) $\dfrac{a^2}{b^2}$, $\dfrac{a}{b}$ times as large

8. $b = \dfrac{ed - ac}{a}$ or $\dfrac{ed}{a} - c$

9. $c = \dfrac{a}{b + a - ab}$

10. (1) 0.82   (2) 0.86   (3) 0.96   (4) 0.97

11. (1) 0.75   (2) 0.89   (3) 0.77

12. (1) $\frac{1}{3}$ (2) 1   (3) $\frac{1}{9}$ (4) $1\frac{1}{9}$ (5) $-\frac{1}{3}$, $\frac{2}{9}$, 0
    (6) Increase, increase, decrease, decrease

Second Test, page 87

1. (1) +	(7) +	(13) +	(19) +
(2) +	(8) +	(14) 0	(20) 0
(3) 0	(9) +	(15) 0	(21) 0
(4) +	(10) 0	(16) +	(22) 0
(5) +	(11) 0	(17) +	(23) +
(6) 0	(12) +	(18) 0	(24) 0

2. $M_1 = \dfrac{N_T M_T - N_2 M_2}{N_1}$

3. $r_2 = \dfrac{n r_1}{1 + (n-1) r_1}$

4. $b = \frac{7}{18}$

5. (1) Increase
   (2) Decrease
   (3) Positive

6. (1) 0
   (2) A fraction smaller than 1
   (3) 1

CHAPTER XI

First Test, page 90

1. a. 1, 6, 7, 8   e. 2, 4, 10
   b. 2, 5, 8, 9   f. 4
   c. 3, 7   g. 1, 6
   d. 1

2. $2y = 3x + 5$

3. (1) $y = 5x + 2$ (2) $y = -\frac{4}{5}x$ or $5y + 4x = 0$

4. $x = 4,\ y = 1$

Exercise 18, page 91

2. $2\frac{1}{2}$, -2, $-\frac{1}{2}$, $2\frac{1}{4}$

3. -3, 1, 6, 1, -4

4. $2+a$, $-3-b$, $-1+c$, $4-d$

5. $+29°$, $+1°$, $-2°$, $-4°$, $+11°$

Exercise 19, page 92

2. (1) East, north   (3) East, south
   (2) West, south   (4) West, north

3. (1) Horizontal, vertical   (8) III
   (2) Horizontal, vertical   (9) I or III
   (3) Vertical, horizontal   (10) Ordinate, abscissa
   (4) Positive, positive   (11) Abscissa, ordinate
   (5) Negative, positive   (12) Abscissa, ordinate
   (6) Negative, negative   (13) Ordinate, abscissa
   (7) Positive, negative

Exercise 20, page 95

3.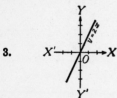

4.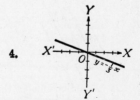

Chapter XI, *continued*

Exercise 20, page 96, *continued*

5.

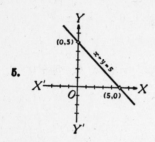

Cross OY at $(0, 5)$
Cross OX at $(5, 0)$
Equation: $x + y = 5$
Indefinitely many pairs of numbers. Yes

6. $x = 2y$ or $y = \frac{1}{2} x$

7. $x + y = 7$

8. All are on a straight line

10. The line is not straight and the equation has a term of second degree

12.
(1) $y = \frac{2}{3} x + \frac{7}{3}$
(2) $y = \frac{1}{4} x^2 + \frac{3}{4} x + 2$
(3) $y = \frac{2}{5} x - 2$
(4) $y = -\frac{1}{5} x + 10$
(5) $y = -\frac{2}{7} x + \frac{20}{7}$
(6) $y = \frac{3}{2} x + 3$
(7) $y = x - 5$
(8) $y = \frac{1}{2} x^2 + 2 x - 6$
(9) $y = \frac{3}{2} x - 5$
(10) $y = \frac{3}{5} x - \frac{4}{5}$
(11) $y = \frac{bx}{a} + \frac{c}{a}$
(12) $y = -\frac{dx}{c} + \frac{k}{c}$

13.
(1)

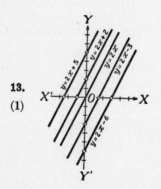

(2)

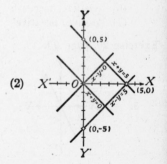

Chapter XI, *continued*

Exercise 20, page 99, *continued*

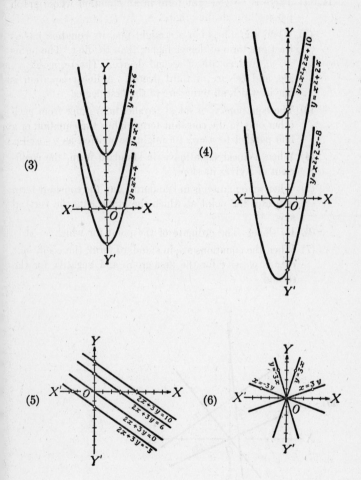

(3)

(4)

(5)

(6)

Exercise 20, page 99, *continued*

14. (1) There is no constant term in an equation whose graph passes through the origin.

(2) When a graph is not a straight line, its equation has at least one term of degree higher than the first. The terms x^2, y^2, and xy are of second degree. The terms x^3, y^3, x^2y, and xy^2 are of third degree. A linear equation is one in which all terms are of the first degree.

(3) The equations of a set of parallel lines differ from each other only in the constant term. Thus the equation of a line parallel to $y = ax + b$ might be written as $y = ax + c$.

(4) When a linear equation is in standard form, the coefficient of x gives its slope.

(5) When an equation is in standard form, the constant term indicates the point at which the graph cuts the vertical axis.

(6) Its slope. The ordinate of the point for which $x = 0$.

(7) When the equations are in standard form, the coefficient of x is positive for the first group and negative for the second.

17.

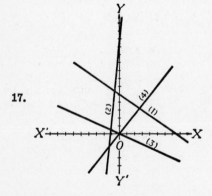

CHAPTER XI, *continued*

Exercise 21, page 103

1. $y = \frac{3}{2}x - \frac{1}{2}$
2. a. $y = 2x + 3$
   b. $y = 1 - x$
   c. $5y = 3x$
   d. $y = \frac{2}{3}x + \frac{5}{3}$

Second Test, page 103

1. a. 4, 5, 6, 10
   b. 1, 4, 7, 8
   c. 6, 9, 11
   d. 6, 10
   e. 2, 7
   f. 3
   g. 5

2. $3y = 2x - 5$

3. (1) $y = 4x - 3$

   (2) $y = \frac{-3x}{7}$ or $7y + 3x = 0$

4. $\begin{cases} x = 5 \\ y = 1 \end{cases}$

CHAPTER XII

First Test, page 105

1. $\sqrt{6}$
2. $\sqrt{a - \dfrac{b}{n}}$
3. $(Nx^2 - a^2)^{\frac{1}{2}}$
4. $\sqrt{\dfrac{1}{cx} - 1}$

5. $\left\{ \dfrac{\sigma_1^2}{2(N_1 - 1)} + \dfrac{\sigma_2^2}{2(N_2 - 1)} \right\}^{\frac{1}{2}}$

6. $\dfrac{ax - bc}{\sqrt{dx - b^2}\ \sqrt{fx - c^2}}$

7. $\frac{1}{15}\sqrt{629}$

Exercise 22, page 109

1. (1) 4.48
   (2) 0.82
   (3) 0.527

   (4) 8.66
   (5) 0.35
   (6) 0.865

2. (1) $\sqrt{\frac{3}{20}}$, half as large
   (2) $\sqrt{\frac{12}{5}}$, twice as large
   (3) $\sqrt{\frac{12}{20}}$, just as large

   (4) 9
   (5) 16

3. (1) 4
   (2) 3
   (3) 3
   (4) 4

   (5) 2
   (6) 2
   (7) 1
   (8) 3

CHAPTER XII, *continued*

Exercise 22, page 110, *continued*

4. (1) 2
    (2) 2
    (3) 1

    (4) 1
    (5) 2
    (6) 2

5. (1) $\frac{1}{4}\sqrt{7}$
    (2) $\frac{1}{25}\sqrt{566}$
    (3) $\frac{1}{8}\sqrt{247}$

    (4) $\frac{1}{20}(2541)^{\frac{1}{2}}$ or $\frac{11}{20}\sqrt{21}$
    (5) $\frac{1}{6}(278)^{\frac{1}{2}}$ or $\frac{1}{6}\sqrt{278}$
    (6) $\frac{1}{8}\sqrt{229}$

6. (1) 0.84   (2) 1.00   (3) 0.10

7. (1) $\sqrt{ab}$
    (2) $\sqrt{\dfrac{ax^2}{n}}$ or $x\sqrt{\dfrac{a}{n}}$
    (3) $\sqrt{ax}$
    (4) $\sqrt{1-ac}$
    (5) $\sqrt{c-ac^2}$

    (6) $\sqrt{ab-cb^2}$
    (7) $\sqrt{a-\dfrac{b^2}{n}}$
    (8) $\sqrt{\dfrac{x}{d}}$
    (9) $\sqrt{3}$
    (10) $\sqrt{6}$

8. $\dfrac{r_{12}-r_{13}r_{23}}{1-r_{23}^2}$

9. (1) $\sqrt{\dfrac{p_1q_1}{n_1}+\dfrac{p_2q_2}{n_2}}$

    (2) $\sqrt{\dfrac{(1-r_1^2)^2}{N}+\dfrac{(1-r_2^2)^2}{N}}$ or $\sqrt{\dfrac{2-2r_1^2+r_1^4-2r_2^2+r_2^4}{N}}$

10. $\sqrt{tq-r^2}$

11. $\sqrt{t-\dfrac{r^2}{q}}$

12. $\dfrac{pq-rs}{\sqrt{tq-r^2}\,\sqrt{uq-s^2}}$

13. $\dfrac{p-\dfrac{rs}{q}}{\sqrt{t-\dfrac{r^2}{q}}\,\sqrt{u-\dfrac{s^2}{q}}}$

14. $\sqrt{N\Sigma(x')^2-(\Sigma x')^2}$

CHAPTER XII, *continued*

Exercise 22, page 113, *continued*

15. $$\dfrac{\Sigma XY - \dfrac{(\Sigma X)(\Sigma Y)}{N}}{\sqrt{\Sigma X^2 - \dfrac{(\Sigma X)^2}{N}}\sqrt{\Sigma Y^2 - \dfrac{(\Sigma Y)^2}{N}}}$$

16. $$\dfrac{N\Sigma XY - (\Sigma X)(\Sigma Y)}{\sqrt{N\Sigma X^2 - (\Sigma X)^2}\sqrt{N\Sigma Y^2 - (\Sigma Y)^2}}$$

17. (1) 0.26   (3) 0.18
    (2) 0.52   (4) Increase, decrease

18. $\dfrac{\sigma_x^2 + \sigma_y^2 - \sigma_{x-y}^2}{2\sigma_x\sigma_y}$

19. (1) 0.047   (2) 0.0059

20. (1) 0.93   (2) 0.82

21. $n = \dfrac{9pq}{(p-0.50)^2}$

Second Test, page 114

1. $\sqrt{15}$ 2. $\sqrt{cr-x}$ 3. $\sqrt{\Sigma X^2 - NM^2}$

4. $\sqrt{1 - \dfrac{1}{ax}}$

5. $\sigma_{x-y} = \sqrt{\dfrac{\sigma_1^2}{N} - \dfrac{2r\sigma_1\sigma_2}{N} - \dfrac{\sigma_2^2}{N}}$ or $\sqrt{\dfrac{\sigma_1^2 - 2r\sigma_1\sigma_2 + \sigma_2^2}{N}}$

6. $\dfrac{\dfrac{a}{d} - \dfrac{bc}{d^2}}{\sqrt{\dfrac{x}{d} - \dfrac{b^2}{d^2}}\sqrt{\dfrac{y}{d} - \dfrac{c^2}{d^2}}}$

7. $\frac{1}{12}\sqrt{617}$

CHAPTER XIII

Exercise 23, page 117

1. $-.3, \ -.3, \ -.3, \ -.3$

2. $x' = x + c_x,$ or $x = x' - c_x,$ or $c_x = x' - x$

Chapter XIII, *continued*

Exercise 24, page 124

1. 5 and 14, 2, 7, 12, 3, 8, 9, 2, 5 and 14, 9, 6, 5 and 14, 1, 4 and 10, 11 and 13

2. (1) $S_7 = X_7 + Y_7 + Z_7 + W_7$

   (2) $D = M_x - M_y$　or　$M_x - M_y = \dfrac{\Sigma X - \Sigma Y}{N}$

   (3) $N_x = N_y = N_z = N_w$.　In this situation the subscripts are not needed.

3. (1) $\Sigma y = 0$

   (2) $M_y = \dfrac{\Sigma Y}{N}$

   (3) $M_y = M'_y + \dfrac{\Sigma y'}{N}$

   (4) $\sigma_y^2 = \dfrac{\Sigma y^2}{N}$

   (5) $\dfrac{\Sigma y^2}{N} < \dfrac{\Sigma (y')^2}{N}$

   (6) $\Sigma f = N$

4. $M_{x+5} = 19.7$　and　$\sigma_{x+5} = 1.42$

5. $M_{x-2} = 12.7$　and　$\sigma_{x-2} = 1.42$

6. $M_{x+a} = M_x + a$,

   $\sigma_{x+a} = \sigma_x$

   To add a constant amount to each score in a distribution increases the mean by the constant amount but does not affect the standard deviation.

8. (2) $N_c = N_B + N_G$
   (3) 73.19
   (4) -0.69
   (5) $d_G = M_G - M_C = 0.41$
   (6) 6.65

9. Only one value of M but an indefinite number of values of M'

Chapter XIV

Exercise 25, page 138

1. Function but not an equation: 3, 4, 7, 8, 9
   Equation: 1, 2, 5, 10, 11, 12, 13, 14, 15
   Conditional equation: 1, 2, 5, 12, 13
   Identity: 10, 11, 14, 15

CHAPTER XIV, *continued*

Exercise 25, page 138, *continued*

2. (1) 1   (7) ∞ (13) 0
   (2) 0   (8) ∞ (14) 6
   (3) ∞ (9) ∞ (15) ∞
   (4) 2   (10) ∞ (16) 1
   (5) 3   (11) ∞ (17) 2
   (6) 4   (12) ∞ (18) 1

3.   *Variables*   *Parameters*
   (1) C, T r, σ_C, σ_T, M_C, M_T
   (2) S, T_1, T_2, T_3 m_1, m_2, m_3
   (3) T, S_1, S_2, S_3 σ_1, σ_2, σ_3

CHAPTER XV

First Test, page 141

1. $n^2 - 2n + 1$

2. $1 - 6a + 9a^2$

3. $16 - 40r + 25r^2$

4. $y^2 - 2rxy + r^2 x^2$

5. $x_1 x_2 + 3x_1 - 2x_2 - 6$

6. $9a^2 + 30a + 25$

7. $9r^2 - 24rn + 16n^2$

8. $2a^2 - 3an - 2n^2$

9. $a - \dfrac{ac}{bd} - \dfrac{bc}{x} + \dfrac{c^2}{dx}$

10. $x_1 x_2 - a_1 x_2 - a_2 x_1 + a_1 a_2$

11. $x_1^2 - 2r_{12}\dfrac{\sigma_1}{\sigma_2}x_1 x_2 + r_{12}^2 \dfrac{\sigma_1^2}{\sigma_2^2}x_2^2$

12. $\dfrac{x}{b} - \dfrac{a}{c} - \dfrac{c}{a} + \dfrac{b}{x}$

13. $n^2 - \dfrac{p^2}{q^2}$

14. $a^2 x_1 x_2 + \dfrac{3a}{2}x_1^2 - \dfrac{2a}{3}x_2^2 - x_1 x_2 = x_1 x_2(a^2 - 1) + \dfrac{3a}{2}x_1^2 - \dfrac{2a}{3}x_2^2$

15. $x_1 x_2 - r_{12}\dfrac{\sigma_1}{\sigma_2}x_2^2 - r_{12}\dfrac{\sigma_2}{\sigma_1}x_1^2 + r_{12}^2 x_1 x_2 = x_1 x_2(1 + r_{12}^2) - r_{12}\left(\dfrac{\sigma_1}{\sigma_2}x_2^2 + \dfrac{\sigma_2}{\sigma_1}x_1^2\right)$

Exercise 26, page 142

1. $5s^2 - 3n^2 - 2r^2 - 14ns + 3rs + 7rn$

2. $2p^2 - 5q^2 - 9pq - p + 5q$

3. $c^3 - 3c^2 + 3c - 1$

4. $a^2 - b^2 + a + 3b - 2$

5. $x^4 - 4x^3y + 6x^2y^2 - 4xy^3 + y^4$

Exercise 27, page 143

1. $9 - 6x_1 + x_1^2$

2. $y^2 - 10ay + 24a^2$

3. $4r^2 - 25$

4. $1 - 6c + 9c^2$

5. $h_1^2 - h_2^2 h_3^2$

6. $1 - 2R_{1\cdot23}^2 + R_{1\cdot23}^4$

7. $1 - \dfrac{cb}{ad} + \dfrac{ad}{b} - c$

8. $x_2 x_3 - a_2 x_3 - a_3 x_2 + a_2 a_3$

9. $y^2 - 2r_{xy}\dfrac{\sigma_y}{\sigma_x}xy + r_{xy}^2\dfrac{\sigma_y^2}{\sigma_x^2}x^2$

10. $xy(1 + r^2) - r\dfrac{\sigma_y}{\sigma_x}x^2 - r\dfrac{\sigma_x}{\sigma_y}y^2$

11. $12n^2 - 7np - 10p^2$

12. $2 + t - 15t^2$

13. $1 - 25x^2$

14. $r_1^2 + n_1 r_1 - 2n_1^2$

15. $(x')^2 - 2x'c + c^2$

16. $X^2 - 2MX + M^2$

17. $XY - M_x Y - M_y X + M_x M_y$

18. $x'y' - c_x y' - c_y x' + c_x c_y$

19. $x_2 x_4 - r_{23}\dfrac{\sigma_2}{\sigma_3}x_3 x_4 - r_{34}\dfrac{\sigma_4}{\sigma_3}x_2 x_3$

$+ r_{23}r_{34}\dfrac{\sigma_2\sigma_4}{\sigma_3^2}x_3^2$

20. $x_5^2 - 2r_{35}\dfrac{\sigma_5}{\sigma_3}x_3 x_5 + r_{35}^2\dfrac{\sigma_5^2}{\sigma_3^2}x_3^2$

Second Test, page 143

1. $1 - 2r^2 + r^4$

2. $9d^2 + 6d + 1$

3. $4 - 4rx + r^2 x^2$

4. $x_1^2 - 2r_{12}x_1 x_2 + r_{12}^2 x_2^2$

5. $y_1 y_2 + y_1 - 7y_2 - 7$

6. $16c^2 - 24c + 9$

7. $25p^2 - 20pq + 4q^2$

8. $r^2 - 9t^2$

9. $n - \dfrac{a}{x} - \dfrac{x^2}{a} + \dfrac{x}{n}$

10. $y_1 y_2 - c_1 y_2 - c_2 y_1 + c_1 c_2$

11. $x_3^2 - 2r_{13}\dfrac{\sigma_3}{\sigma_1}x_1 x_3 + r_{13}^2\dfrac{\sigma_3^2}{\sigma_1^2}x_1^2$

12. $\dfrac{n}{2} - \dfrac{n^2}{4} - \dfrac{2}{9}$

13. $c^2 - \dfrac{r^2}{n^2}$

14. $\dfrac{4}{9}x_1^2 - 2x_1 + 2$

15. $y_1 y_3 - r_{12}\dfrac{\sigma_1}{\sigma_2}y_2 y_3 - r_{23}\dfrac{\sigma_3}{\sigma_2}y_1 y_2$

$+ r_{12}r_{23}\dfrac{\sigma_1\sigma_3}{\sigma_2^2}y_2^2$

CHAPTER XVI

First Test, page 144

1. (1) $a(x_1+x_2+x_3)$

(2) $\sigma_1^2(1-r_{12}^2)$

(3) $b(x_1y_1+x_2y_2+x_3y_3+x_4y_4)$

(4) $3n(2r-t+n)$

(5) $\sigma_1(\sigma_1+\sigma_2r_{12}+\sigma_3r_{13})$

(6) $b(A_1+A_2+A_3)$

(7) $n(p_1q_1+p_2q_2+p_3q_3)$

(8) $\sigma_2(\sigma_2+R_{2\cdot3})$

(9) $\dfrac{1}{n}(a+b+c)$

(10) $x(r_1+r_2+r_3)$

(11) $5(a^2+b^2+c^2)$

(12) $N(a+b)$

2. (1) $-$ (6) $+$ (11) $+$ (16) $-$

(2) $+$ (7) $-$ (12) $-$ (17) $-$

(3) $-$ (8) $+$ (13) $-$ (18) $+$

(4) $+$ (9) $+$ (14) $+$ (19) $-$

(5) $+$ (10) $+$ (15) $+$ (20) $+$

3. (1) $r_{12}\sigma_1\sigma_2+bc$

(2) $\sigma_1^2(1-r_{12}^2)$

(3) $\sigma_1\sigma_3(r_{13}-r_{12}r_{23})$

Exercise 28, page 147

1. $5(a_1+2a_2+5a_3)$

2. $4(ab+bc+ac)$

3. $\dfrac{a}{3}(b+c+d)$

4. $a(b_1+b_2+b_3)$

5. $b(a_1+a_2+a_3)$

6. $2r_{13}(r_{12}+2r_{15})$

7. $\sigma_1^2(1+r_1+r_1^2)$

8. $x(n_1+n_2+n_3+n_4)$

9. $N(M_1+M_2+M_3)$

10. $2k(1+k+2k^2)$

11. $\sigma_1^2(1-n_{12}^2)$

12. $\dfrac{p}{q^2}(q+p)$ or $\dfrac{p}{q}\left(1+\dfrac{p}{q}\right)$

13. $a(x_1y_1+x_2y_2+x_3y_3)$

14. $a(t_1+t_2+t_3)$

15. $a(t_1s_1+t_2s_2+t_3s_3)$

16. $ts(a_1+a_2+a_3)$

17. $c(x_1x_2+x_1x_3+x_2x_3)$

18. $n(X_1+X_2+X_3)$

19. $r(p_1q_1+p_2q_2+p_3q_3)$

20. $(r_1-2r_2)\sqrt{1-r_1^2}$

Exercise 29, page 149

1. $f_1x_1y_1+f_2x_2y_2+f_3x_3y_3+f_4x_4y_4$

2. $a(x_1+x_2+\cdots+x_N)$

3. $w_1+w_2+\cdots+w_N+Nc$

4. $y_5^2+y_6^2+y_7^2-2c(y_5+y_6+y_7)+3c^2$

5. $3(z_1+z_2+z_3+\cdots+z_N)+3aN$

Chapter XVI, *continued*

Exercise 29, page 150, *continued*

6. $z_6^2+z_7^2+z_8^2+z_9^2-2t(z_6w_6+z_7w_7+z_8w_8+z_9w_9)$
$$+t^2(w_6^2+w_7^2+w_8^2+w_9^2)$$

7. $w_1x_1^2+w_2x_2^2+\cdots+w_Nx_N^2-2a(x_1w_1+x_2w_2+\cdots+x_Nw_N)$
$$+a^2(w_1+w_2+\cdots+w_N)$$

8. $(x_9y_9+x_{10}y_{10}+x_{11}y_{11}+x_{12}y_{12})+b(x_9+x_{10}+x_{11}+x_{12})$
$$+a(y_9+y_{10}+y_{11}+y_{12})+4ab$$

9. $(x_1^2+x_2^2+\cdots+x_N^2)-2b(x_1w_1+x_2w_2+\cdots+x_Nw_N)$
$$+b^2(w_1^2+w_2^2+\cdots+w_N^2)$$

10. $(x_1y_1+x_2y_2+\cdots+x_Ny_N)-c_x(y_1+y_2+\cdots+y_N)$
$$-c_y(x_1+x_2+\cdots+x_N)+Nc_xc_y$$

Exercise 30, page 151

1. $\Sigma x+2\Sigma y+N$
2. $\Sigma xy-c\Sigma x-c\Sigma y+Nc^2$
3. $\Sigma x^2-2a\Sigma x+Na^2$
4. $a\Sigma x-a^2\Sigma y$
5. $\Sigma x^2-2d\Sigma xw+d^2\Sigma w^2$
6. $\Sigma x^3-3c\Sigma x^2+3c^2\Sigma x-Nc^3$
7. $\Sigma x'-\Sigma x+aN$
8. $\Sigma wy^2-2b\Sigma wy+b^2\Sigma w$
9. Na
10. $\Sigma w+Nc$
11. Nab
12. $a\Sigma x-Na$

Exercise 31, page 153

1. M_2
2. NM_2
3. σ_3^2
4. $r_{23}\sigma_2\sigma_3$
5. $N\sigma_4^2$
6. 0
7. 0
8. $r_{13}\sigma_1\sigma_3$
9. $Nr_{34}\sigma_3\sigma_4$
10. $Nr_{14}\sigma_1\sigma_4$
11. $Nb\sigma_2^2$
12. NM_3
13. 0
14. 0
15. $ar_{12}\sigma_1\sigma_2$
16. 0
17. $r_{12}^2\sigma_1\sigma_2$
18. $r_{12}\dfrac{\sigma_1}{\sigma_2}$
19. $r\sigma_2\sigma_3$
20. $r_{32}r_{12}\sigma_1\sigma_3$

Second Test, page 158

1. (1) $2(x_1^2+x_2^2+x_3^2)$
   (2) $c(x_1y_1+x_2y_2+x_3y_3)$
   (3) $x(a_1+a_2+a_3)$
   (4) $5p(2q-1+3p)$
   (5) $a^2(b_1+b_2+b_3+b_4)$
   (6) $r_1(1-r_1)$
   (7) $c(X_1+X_2+X_3+X_4)$
   (8) $M_1(a+b+c)$
   (9) $\sigma_1^2(1-r^2-R^2)$
   (10) $\sigma_1^2(1-R_{1.23}^2)$
   (11) $\dfrac{1}{a}(x+y)$
   (12) $pq(n_1+n_2+n_3)$

CHAPTER XVI, *continued*

Second Test, page 159, *continued*

2. (1) $+$ (11) $-$ **3.** (1) σ^2+a^2

(2) $-$ (12) $+$ (2) $\sigma_1^2+2r_{12}\sigma_1\sigma_2+\sigma_2^2$

(3) $-$ (13) $+$ (3) $r_{12}\sigma_1\sigma_2(r_{12}^2-1)$

(4) $-$ (14) $+$

(5) $+$ (15) $+$

(6) $-$ (16) $+$

(7) $-$ (17) $-$

(8) $+$ (18) $-$

(9) $+$ (19) $+$

(10) $+$ (20) $-$

CHAPTER XVII

First Test, page 161

1. (1) 1   (11) $\frac{1}{16}$ (21) $\frac{1}{8}$

(2) $\frac{1}{4}$ (12) 4   (22) 16

(3) 2   (13) 1   (23) 64

(4) $\frac{1}{2}$ (14) 16   (24) 8

(5) $\frac{1}{8}$ (15) 256   (25) $\frac{1}{8}$

(6) 8   (16) 16   (26) $\frac{1}{3}$

(7) 1   (17) $\frac{1}{2}$ (27) 1

(8) $-\frac{1}{4}$ (18) 16   (28) 1

(9) $\frac{1}{16}$ (19) $\frac{1}{4}$ (29) 16

(10) $-\frac{1}{64}$ (20) $\frac{1}{128}$ (30) 1

2. (1) $10^{2.64}$ (3) $10^{-0.43}$ (5) $10^{0.2}$

(2) $10^{2.58}$ (4) $10^{-0.5}$ (6) $10^{0.65}$

Exercise 33, page 165

1. (1) $\dfrac{1}{r^3}$ (5) $x^{\frac{2}{3}}$ (9) $a^{-\frac{1}{2}}$ (13) c^2

(2) $\sqrt{a}$ (6) a (10) b^{-2} (14) $a^{-\frac{1}{2}}$

(3) 1   (7) x^{-4} (11) $a^{\frac{5}{4}}$ (15) $x^{\frac{3}{2}}$

(4) $\dfrac{1}{c^4}$ (8) $n^{\frac{5}{2}}$ (12) ab^{-1} (16) $\sqrt[7]{x^3}$

CHAPTER XVII, *continued*

Exercise 33, page 166, *continued*

3. (1) 16
   (2) 20
   (3) $\frac{1}{20}$
   (4) 1
   (5) 3
   (6) $\frac{1}{5}$
   (7) 9
   (8) 16
   (9) 8
   (10) 6
   (11) 7
   (12) 25
   (13) 2
   (14) $\frac{1}{25}$
   (15) $\frac{1}{3}$

4. (1) $10^{1.26}$
   (2) $10^{0.14}$
   (3) $10^{2.83}$
   (4) $10^{-3.71}$
   (5) $10^{0.57}$
   (6) $10^{1.788}$
   (7) $10^{0.48}$
   (8) $10^{1.5}$
   (9) $10^{0.333}$
   (10) $10^{0.25}$
   (11) $10^{0.125}$
   (12) $10^{-0.5}$
   (13) $10^{-0.333}$
   (14) $10^{-0.25}$
   (15) $10^{0.75}$

5. (1) $-\frac{1}{2}$
   (2) $\frac{1}{16}$
   (3) 1
   (4) -2
   (5) -1
   (6) $\frac{1}{36}$
   (7) $\frac{1}{81}$
   (8) $-\frac{1}{27}$
   (9) $-\frac{1}{2}$

Second Test, page 167

1. (1) 1
   (2) 3
   (3) $\frac{1}{27}$
   (4) 1
   (5) $-\frac{1}{729}$
   (6) 9
   (7) 81
   (8) 81
   (9) $\frac{1}{243}$
   (10) 81
   (11) 81
   (12) 27
   (13) 1
   (14) 1
   (15) $\frac{1}{27}$
   (16) 8
   (17) $\frac{1}{2}$
   (18) 27
   (19) $\frac{1}{9}$
   (20) $\frac{1}{3}$
   (21) 27
   (22) $-\frac{1}{9}$
   (23) $\frac{1}{81}$
   (24) 81
   (25) $\frac{1}{81}$
   (26) 1
   (27) 81
   (28) $\frac{1}{3}$
   (29) $\frac{1}{81}$
   (30) $\frac{1}{27}$

2. (1) $10^{1.84}$
   (2) $10^{1.51}$
   (3) $10^{-0.97}$
   (4) $10^{-0.333}$
   (5) $10^{0.125}$
   (6) $10^{-0.34}$

CHAPTER XVIII

First Test, page 168

1. 16.34
2. 3.145
3. 1.518
4. 0.02142
5. 0.1963
6. 2.419

CHAPTER XVIII, *continued*

Exercise 34, page 169

1. (1) 8   (2) −2   (3) −4   (4) −7

2. (1) 16   (4) 65536   (7) 0.125
   (2) 131072   (5) 0.03125   (8) 0.25
   (3) 64   (6) 262144

3. (1) Add   (5) Multiply, by 2
   (2) Subtract, from   (6) Multiply, by n
   (3) Divide, by 3   (7) Divide, by n
   (4) Divide, by 5

Exercise 35, page 171

1. 421.7   4. 17.78   7. 4.217   10. 2.371
2. 237.1   5. 74.99   8. 237.1
3. 74.99   6. 316.2   9. 1

Exercise 36, page 173

1. (1) 3   (6) 1   (11) −3
   (2) 2   (7) 0   (12) −1
   (3) −5   (8) 0   (13) −5
   (4) 0   (9) 0   (14) 0
   (5) 4   (10) 1   (15) 1

2. (1) $(5.327)(10^3)$ (9) $(9.16)(10^0)$
   (2) $(4.9016)(10^2)$ (10) $(9.16)(10^1)$
   (3) $(1.3)(10^{-5})$ (11) $(3.7)(10^{-3})$
   (4) $(5.1002)(10^0)$ (12) $(3.4)(10^{-1})$
   (5) $(6.21394)(10^4)$ (13) $(4)(10^{-5})$
   (6) $(1.206)(10^1)$ (14) $(4.0003)(10^0)$
   (7) $(3.09)(10^0)$ (15) $(5.131)(10^1)$
   (8) $(1.03)(10^0)$

3. They are the same.

Exercise 37, page 176

2. (1) 2.2856   (4) 0.0374   (7) 1.4099
   (2) 4.3979   (5) $\bar{3}.6021$ (8) 0.5658
   (3) $\bar{2}.2041$ (6) 4.3010   (9) 1.1367

3. (1) 4.9   (4) .00399   (7) 92.7
   (2) 5480   (5) 7.02   (8) 690
   (3) 15.3   (6) .553   (9) .0559

CHAPTER XVIII, *continued*

Exercise 38, page 177

1. (1) 3.9496
(2) 1.0924
(3) 0.6024

(4) 5.8581
(5) $\bar{2}$.0592
(6) $\bar{1}$.3718

(7) 0.5788
(8) 0.6703
(9) 2.2390

2. (1) 4221
(2) 10.94

(3) .6628
(4) .04182

(5) 1.387
(6) 23.01

Exercise 39, page 179

1. 2.142
2. .2713
3. 19.93
4. .001698

5. .8258
6. 131.5
7. 53.74

8. .2059
9. 2.021
10. 44.79

Second Test, page 179

1. 1.218
2. 21.42

3. 0.00003038
4. 0.03232

5. 0.759
6. 1.021

CHAPTER XIX

First Test, page 180

1. 1, 4, 6, 7, 9, 10
2. 1, 3, 5, 6, 7, 9
3. $\sigma_{2\cdot345} = \sigma_2\sqrt{1-r_{23}^2}\ \sqrt{1-r_{24\cdot3}^2}\ \sqrt{1-r_{25\cdot34}^2}$
4. 2, 4
5. x_5 is unique variable, r_{46} is unique r
6. x_1 and x_4

Exercise 40, page 186

1. 7
2. 8
3. 6
4. 5

5. 6
6. 2
7. 1
8. 3

9. 0
10. 7
11. $\frac{2}{3}$
12. 12

13. $a+b$
14. 0
15. 4
16. 0

Exercise 41, page 190

1. (1) 1
(2) 2
(3) 0
(4) 0

(5) 4
(6) 5
(7) 0

(8) 2
(9) 0
(10) 1

Chapter XIX, *continued*

Exercise 41, page 190, *continued*

2.
(1) 6	(4) 9	(7) 1	(10) $n-m$
(2) $n+m$	(5) 2	(8) 1	(11) 0
(3) 2	(6) 4	(9) 6	(12) 0

3. 1, 4, 5, 7, 8, 10, 13, 15

4. $\sigma_{4\cdot215} = \sigma_4 \sqrt{1-r_{42}^2}\ \sqrt{1-r_{41\cdot2}^2}\ \sqrt{1-r_{45\cdot21}^2}$

$\sigma_{3\cdot12} = \sigma_3 \sqrt{1-r_{31}^2}\ \sqrt{1-r_{32\cdot1}^2}$

$\sigma_{6\cdot789} = \sigma_6 \sqrt{1-r_{67}^2}\ \sqrt{1-r_{68\cdot7}^2}\ \sqrt{1-r_{69\cdot78}^2}$

5. $R_{2(34)} = \left\{ 1-(1-r_{23}^2)(1-r_{24\cdot3}^2) \right\}^{\frac{1}{2}}$

$R_{5(4)} = \left\{ 1-(1-r_{54}^2) \right\}^{\frac{1}{2}} = r_{54}$

$R_{3(256)} = \left\{ 1-(1-r_{32}^2)(1-r_{35\cdot2}^2)(1-r_{36\cdot25}^2) \right\}^{\frac{1}{2}}$

6.

	Symmetrical	*Unique*
(1)	$x,\ z$	y
(2)	$z,\ w$	v
(3)	$z,\ w$	$x,\ y$
(4)	$v,\ w$	x
(5)	$x,\ w$	y
(6)	$x_4,\ x_2$	$x_3,\ x_6$
(7)	$x_4,\ x_5$	$x_2,\ x_3$

Second Test, page 191

1. 2, 4, 6, 7, 9

2. 1, 4, 5, 6, 7

3. $R_{3(124)} = \left\{ 1-(1-r_{31}^2)(1-r_{32\cdot1}^2)(1-r_{34\cdot12}^2) \right\}^{\frac{1}{2}}$

4. 1, 3

5. x_2 is unique variable

r_{13} is unique r

6. x_3 and x_4

Chapter XX

Exercise 42, page 198

1. $y = -2.1x + 2.7$

2. $y = 0.70x + 5.14$

3. $y = -3x$

4. $y = 2.51x - 0.086$

Chapter XXI

Exercise 43, page 211

1. (1) .0102
   (2) .0105
   (3) .8030
   (4) .7959

   (5) .0968
   (6) .8997
   (7) .8962
   (8) .0918

2. $\pm 0.6588\sigma$
3. $+0.6840\sigma$
4. -0.6776σ
5. $+0.6620\sigma$
6. -0.6871σ

7. (1) 109.45 to 117.15
   (2) 109.59 to 117.01
   (3) .8944 or 89%
   (4) 117.13
   (5) 109.58
   (6) 109.47
   (7) 117.09
   (8) 109.52 to 117.08

8.

$\frac{x}{\sigma}$	Area between 0 and $\frac{x}{\sigma}$
1.332	.4085
0.660	.2454
1.257	.3957
0.670	.2486
1.282	.4000
0.672	.2493
1.322	.4070
0.686	.2536

INDEX